BETTER
SHORTWAVE
RECEPTION

WILLIAM I. ORR,   W6SAI, KCK 3201
STUART D. COWAN,   W2LX, KCZ 1102

RADIO PUBLICATIONS, INC.
BOX 149, WILTON, CONN. 06897

BETTER SHORTWAVE RECEPTION

Library of Congress Catalog Card Number 57-14916

Fourth Edition
Second Printing-1977

TABLE OF CONTENTS

FOREWORD

A new world of thrills greets the armchair adventurer who tunes in radio signals "above" and "below" the ends of the dial of a standard broadcast receiver. Gone are the familiar entertainment programs and in their place are thousands of strange, interesting transmissions.

The hobby of radio eavesdropping is increasingly popular in today's world of science and space travel. Forty years ago, relatively few "shortwave listeners" pursued an avocation which seemed too complicated and expensive for most people. Today this misconception has been swept away -- we live in a communications-oriented world. Inexpensive transistor radios cover several shortwave bands. Millions of people are aware of amateur radio and citizens band radio, and more men and women hold these licenses to broadcast than at any time in history.

As with other hobbies, knowledge is essential to further the advance of the enthusiast. This book is, we hope, such a tool. It is more than simply a guide to international broadcasting. In it, you'll find information on the electromagnetic spectrum from 10 kc to microwaves. And you'll pick up practical tips which take years to learn the hard way.

In recent years, the term "cycles per second" in conjunction with radio waves has been supplanted by "Hertz" in honor of the 19th century Austrian physicist, Heinrich Hertz, who conducted early radio experiments. Thus, *cycles per second* became *Hertz; kilocycles* became *kilohertz* (1,000 cycles); and *megacycles* became *megahertz* (1,000,000 cycles). In this book, however, the older and more common terms, cycles, kilocycles (kc) and megacycles (mc), are used in most places.

The authors hope that this handbook will serve as your guide to an exciting journey into the world of radio communications. And who knows where this interest may lead -- to your amateur operator's license, to a career in radio, television, medical electronics, space electronics, data processing or other challenging fields which depend upon the miracle of the unseen electron!

William I. Orr
Stuart D. Cowan

CHAPTER 1

Listen To The World

Come with us, away from the cares of everyday living, on a trip of relaxation and high adventure — right in your own home! Follow us down the electronic pathway of mysterious radio waves to far-off lands, to ships at sea, to scientists in the subzero Antarctic, to radio amateurs talking with far corners of the earth. Hear ancient church bells from the BBC in London mark the hour, listen to the first bars of "The East is Red" from Radio Peking. Tune in an Air Force jet winging over the Pacific, listen to a missionary high in the Andes talking to loved ones back home. Judge for yourself how the Soviet Union and China react to political events in the U.S. The world is truly at your fingertips with a shortwave radio receiver!

The glamor and excitement of listening directly to exciting world events appeals to young and old, students, business and professional men and women —just about everyone! Radio eavesdropping, which is perfectly legal, offers rewards to handicapped people confined to their homes and to retired senior citizens who seek new interests at modest cost. An important and satisfying hobby, shortwave listening may well be the first step toward your amateur radio license—transforming you from a listener to a participant in the exciting radio world.

THE RADIO SPECTRUM

The hobby is known as "shortwave listening" and one who pursues it is an "SWL" or "shortwave listener." In recent years interest has expanded to other frequencies even though the high frequency (HF) radio bands still offer the most consistent fare for the average SWL. There is a lot to listen to on other frequencies, and still more if one learns the International radio-telegraph code which is *not* difficult in spite of what you may have heard! The frequency bands in the radio spectrum are as follows:

VOICE OF AMERICA, the radio section of the United States Information Service, speaks to the world in over 40 languages over a network of 78 transmitters located in the United States and various foreign countries. Four outlets (Munich, Germany; Luzon, Philippines; Okinawa and Thailand) have million-watt facilities.

The Voice's headquarters are located in Washington, D. C., the point of origin for most of the daily programs. Shown above is the master control desk—the technical heart and brain of the VOA. Selection of programs from 100 different sources for 26 separate transmissions may be made at one time. Direct lines to the White House, the United Nations, radio centers in Munich and Paris, and commercial networks permit up-to-the-minute selection of important news events and happenings in all parts of the world.

Installation of the control board took a crew of engineers more than a year. It involved the use of over 375 miles of shielded wire and nearly 30 miles of 20 conductor cable with more than 5 million connections. The board is manned at all times by at least two technicians.

(1) *Very Low Frequencies (VLF), 10 kc to 550 kc.* These very long waves carry interesting transmissions but they are mostly in International Morse code and radioteletype (RTTY). The Navy uses these very low frequencies to contact nuclear submarines. If you can copy CW (continuous wave, i.e., the code) you will pick up marine hydrographic messages, ice warnings, and messages from commercial vessels; you will also hear marine beacon stations and some aviation weather. It is against the law to divulge the contents of messages you hear on any frequency. Please see chapter 10 for further information.

(2) *Medium Frequencies (MF), the "Broadcast Band," 540 kc to 1600 kc.* This is the band which everyone knows, where standard entertainment AM broadcasting stations live.

(3) *High Frequencies (HF), 1.6 mc to 30 mc.* The shortwave spectrum starts at the "top" of the broadcast band (1,600 kilocycles, or 1.6 mc) and extends up to 30,000 kilocycles, or 30 mc. (a kilocycle or kilohertz is 1,000 cycles; a megacycle or megahertz is 1,000,000 cycles; they are abbreviated "kcs" and "kHz", and "mc" or "MHz", respectively). It is this broad expanse of frequencies which is of greatest interest to most SWLs for it is a smorgasbord of fascinating, long distance radio fare. International broadcasting takes place here. The types of signals you encounter on these frequencies are discussed later in this chapter, and in chapter 9.

(4) *Very High Frequencies (VHF), 30 mc to 300 mc.* Shortwave listening has grown rapidly in this range of frequencies as good, low-cost imported receivers became available. VHF signals are largely line-of-sight but the use of "repeaters" — high-power transmitters which automatically rebroadcast weaker signals — can extend the radio range to one hundred miles or so.

On the VHF bands you will hear police, fire department, weather, marine, commercial and private aircraft, trucks, trains, and amateur radio communications. Many of these transmissions are of extremely short duration, often a matter of a few seconds, and are difficult to intercept. Your problem is to *find* transmissions of interest among the vast array of frequencies—the "needle in the haystack" problem!

RADIO ANDORRA, broadcasting from tiny country high in the Pyrenees Mountains is rare DX catch for shortwave listener. One of the hundreds of stations received in the U.S., "Roc des Anelletas" transmits sponsored programs, contrasted to great majority of broadcasters that are government controlled.

To help SWLs find VHF signals of interest, a new breed of "scanning" receivers has been developed. These ingenious receivers automatically listen on one frequency and if nothing is heard, jump to the next frequency, the next, and so on, in rapid succession . . . and then start sampling the frequencies all over again. On some receivers, colored lights flash on and off, indicating the channel being scanned. When the receiver locates a signal, it stops scanning and stays with the signal until it finishes. Then the receiver starts checking each frequency again.

You do not, of course, have to buy a scanning receiver; you may use a manually tuned, continuous coverage VHF receiver, and many listeners do. The dial is roughly calibrated in MHz (megahertz) or Mc (megacycles, the same thing.) VHF frequencies are expressed as, 162.55 MHz.

Some VHF receivers have only two VHF bands. "High Band" (about 144-170 MHz) and "Low Band" (about 30-50 MHz). These two bands embrace the portions of the VHF spectrum with the most (but not all) activity. Most of these receivers also have "Squelch" which is very desirable on VHF; this is a circuit which keeps the loudspeaker silent except when a

GIANT DIRECTIONAL ANTENNAS are used to transmit shortwave broadcasts to all points of the world. "Beamed" signal follows great circle route from transmitter to your receiver. The ionized layer of air above the earth reflects radio signals back to the earth, much like a mirror, permitting shortwave broadcasts to cover areas of many thousands of miles. Shown above is one of the many Voice of America's stations in the United States. The site of this "curtain array" is Delano, Calif., beaming programs to Asia and the Far East.

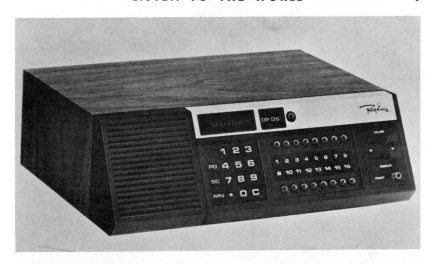

REGENCY "Touch" VHF-UHF 3-band scanning receiver can search out over 15,000 frequencies at the touch of a finger. When it locates a busy channel, it stops to listen and resumes the hunt when the signal goes off the air.

signal is received, so that you do not constantly hear the annoying "rushing" noise in the loudspeaker when no signals are on the air.

(5) *Ultra High Frequencies (UHF), 300 mc to 3,000 mc.* Few SWLs are equipped to listen on these extremely high frequencies which require sophisticated, low-noise receivers and elaborate high-gain receiving antennas which preferably can be both rotated and tilted. The dollar investment can be substantial. Nevertheless, a few skilled SWLs and radio hams do monitor UHF and are rewarded with unusual results.

Properly equipped, an SWL in this band can hear space craft directly, signals relayed by satellites, and radio astronomy. A few advanced amateurs are even copying facsimile weather maps transmitted back to earth by weather satellites.

What Type of HF Receiver?

Before taking an imaginary trip on the HF shortwave bands, let's summarize the different types of receivers available. The *type* of receiver has a great deal to do with how well you hear stations your receiver can detect. Don't be misled by the exotic foreign names printed on the dial glass — it's far easier to print "Vatican City", "Japan" and "New Delhi" on the dial than to produce a clear signal from these locations! There are three types of HF receivers:

(1) *Inexpensive, "all-band" portable receiver.* These imported receivers have several shortwave bands marked on the dial face, which normally cover only part of the HF spectrum. These sets, which cost $50 to $100 receive the more powerful international broadcasting stations quite well but cannot receive single sideband (SSB) voice signals or CW (radiotelegraph) stations. Neither do they have provision, in most cases, for the use of standard headphones.

WORLD-FAMOUS AMATEUR STATION, W6AM, of California operated by Don Wallace is heard on all amateur bands. Wallace has acres of huge rhombic antennas covering a whole hill on California peninsula. W6AM has contacted most of the countries in the world over a period of 50 years. The station operates on SSB and c-w. Wallace also has extensive ham set in his auto.

While such a receiver is an inexpensive way to start listening to overseas broadcasts, it is not sufficiently selective or sensitive for serious SWLing, and the lack of code reception is a distinct handicap. In addition, serious SWLing cannot be done using an indoor "rabbit ears" antenna; some sets have a jack for an outdoor wire antenna.

(2) *Medium-priced, "all band" portable receiver.* These receivers, also usually imported, cost anything from $125 to $300. They feature improved selectivity and sensitivity, and usually have a BFO control to permit reception of SSB and CW signals. Some have a headphone jack, and a provision for an outdoor antenna which is a "must" for good reception. Many of these sets can also tune portions of the VHF band; you need a special VHF antenna for best results—the little extension-type indoor antennas do not work well.

Receivers in this class are quite satisfactory for those who wish primarily to listen to major foreign broadcasting stations beaming programs to the U.S. They are not satisfactory for the person who wants a truly first-rate receiver with good selectivity (the ability to separate stations close to each other in frequency) and good sensitivity (the ability to pick up weak signals).

The accuracy of the dial calibration of these receivers, and of those in group 1, is not very reliable and you never know exactly what frequency you are receiving; this is a major handicap when you are searching for a particular station.

(3) *High-priced Communications Receiver.* Receivers in this category are for the serious SWL and are manufactured both in the U.S. and abroad.

POPULAR ALLIED SX-190 solid state receiver is typical of high quality short wave set. Receiver features bandspread on s-w broadcast bands, crystal calibrator, S-meter and special SSB detector. Receiver is imported.

Prices of new receivers run from about $300 to well over $1,000 (used receivers are less). You can also build a good receiver from a kit *providing* you are a careful, precise workman and have had experience in building electronic kits.

These receivers have all the necessary controls and refinements, and dial calibration is quite accurate. You may purchase them from dealers who sell amateur equipment, and from the large electronic mail order companies which publish extensive catalogs.

A correctly designed and installed outdoor antenna is essential for serious shortwave reception and is particularly important for VHF and UHF. Don't believe anyone who tells you that all you need is a hunk of wire tossed on the floor!

The serious SWL will have a set of headphones handy to use with weak stations and when interference is heavy.

TUNING THE HF BANDS

The HF world is many times larger than the standard broadcast band and crammed into it is a variety of unusual signals, from clandestine "underground" stations and stuttering radio teletype to Coast Guard cutters on ice patrol and Radio Moscow. A spin across the dial highlights the surprises which await you.

Bidding goodbye to the last broadcasting station at about 1,600 kc, we enter a strange new world. The first inhabitants are buzz saw navigation

PRETTY RADIO HAM Mary Gonsalves of Arizona has worked all states in first few months of amateur activity. Young lady (YL) amateurs have radio club of their own and talk to other YL's on the DX bands.

beacons and LORAN (Long Range Navigation) stations which enable ships and aircraft to pinpoint their positions to within a few hundred yards! Nearby is the 160 meter amateur band with its voice and CW signals, almost buried beneath the crackling beacons.

Slightly higher in frequency are the marine operators of telephone companies ("This is the New York marine operator calling the yacht *Good Time Charlie*). Pleasure craft, work boats and ocean-going ships place telephone calls on these frequencies. Some of the conversations with wife, girl friend or office, and the work boats gossiping among themselves, dish up rare tidbits! On the East coast, you can listen to the Soviet Union's vast fishing fleet — how's your Russian?

Sandwiched in with all this are the aviation weather stations using voice signals which let you check weather at widely scattered points ("Cleveland, ceiling one five thousand, scattered, smoke and haze; visibility three; dew point two point three; wind two eight zero at twelve . . .").

Next comes the 80 meter amateur band filled with chattering CW signals and hundreds of SSB voice signals. Above 4 mc is a Navy shore station calling a ship at sea; at precisely 5 mc is WWV, Fort Collins, Colo., the frequency and time station of the U.S. Bureau of Standards; WWV also broadcasts on exactly 2.5, 10 and 15 mc. Dotting the dial are fast RTTY and other signals that sound like cloth ripping or screaming buzz-saws; the RTTY is sending either plain English or cipher text at 100-150 words per minute; the other mysterious signals may be military computers talking to each other in digital language, secure from prying ears.

Around 6 mc you hear the first loud international broadcasting signals (49 meters) and commercial jets whistling on their way to exotic cities like Rome and Honolulu.

Up to about 25 mc you hear a jungle of CW, RTTY and digital transmissions. Interlaced with these fast, authoritative signals are the amateur radio bands and international broadcasting by over 100 countries.

DELUXE LISTENING POST of Floyd Bacus (Virginia) has logged over 200 countries on the shortwave bands. Three receivers are used with 110 foot wire antenna. QSL cards verifying reception of DX stations adorn the walls.

INTERNATIONAL BROADCASTING

Listening to the viewpoints of other countries is increasingly important in the modern world and rare is the country, no matter how small, which does not wish to talk to the world through its own shortwave broadcasting station.

Your first thrill may come when the powerful voice of Radio Moscow or the British Broadcasting Corporation booms from your loudspeaker while your friends marvel in silence. Radio Peking comes in quite well but its signals travel a harsher radio path and are apt to have a rapid flutter. Major foreign stations broadcast in the language of the country to which they beam their signals so don't worry if your Russian or Chinese is rusty; the announcers speak better English than some of us!

News, talk shows, plays, opera, popular music, cultural programs, language lessons, answers to SWL letters, and political propaganda — all are features of the competing foreign stations.

There are seven principal shortwave broadcast bands: 13, 16, 19, 25, 31, 41 and 49 meter bands. The exact frequency in kilocycles or kilohertz of the transmitter *within* each band enables you to locate the station precisely, *providing* your receiver dial calibration is accurate, which is often not the case, and providing the station is on frequency, which is not always so. There are many stations to choose from; if a signal is fluttery or you experience interference on one band, look for the same signal on another band. Some SWLs have logged over 200 countries! If you know a foreign language or

QSL bureau for Central Radio Club of Soviet Union exhibits typical stacks of QSL cards bound for foreign stations. Shortwave listening is very popular hobby in USSR.

two, so much the better. When you send the stations reception reports, you will usually receive a colorful QSL (acknowledgement) card.

The Amateur Radio Service

By international agreement, amateur radio operators ("amateur" in the sense that they do not accept compensation for their services) have been assigned narrow frequency bands for their own stations. These "hams" engage in a variety of activities: rag-chewing, message handling, RTTY, equipment design and construction, VHF, and UHF tests, DX (talking to distant countries), emergency communications in disasters, slow-scan TV, medical and missionary nets, etc. There are 285,000 amateurs in the U.S. and over 200,000 in the rest of the world.

Listening to ham transmissions interests some SWLs although many of these conversations are something less than dramatic. On the DX bands — 20, 15 and 10 meters — you are more apt to hear interesting exchanges. Many ham SSB signals come in with amazing clarity and patient combing of the DX bands will turn up hundreds of foreign countries, and some conversations which are not dry as dust! Here is KC4USN at the geographic South Pole in QSO (contact) with an Iowa farmer: "Temperature is −110°, and they are flying in an ice cream machine this afternoon . . ."). King Hussein of Jordan, call letters JY1, is chattering with a girl in Philadelphia who calls him "Your Majesty," although he asked to be called "Hussein."

You can strike up friendships almost anywhere on earth via amateur radio, true "people-to-people" communications! Just being a radio ham creates an instant bond between people of different civilizations. Let us encourage *you* to eventually become a radio amateur with your own shortwave transmitting station. It is both a service and a hobby which benefits the world through almost half a million men and women. For information on how to obtain your FCC amateur license, write the American Radio Relay League, 225 Main St.,

MICROWAVE relay towers used for point-to-point transmission of VOA programs from studio to station site in Philippines.

Newington, CT 06111. It may be one of the most rewarding things you ever did!

Shortwave listening offers you unending variety and a modest quotient of excitement, ranging from the calm feminine voice directing a police cruiser on its journey of justice to a North African station's native music that sounds like six cats in a brawl . . . radio amateurs arranging urgent air shipment of a scarce drug to save the life of a little boy in Peru . . . loved ones brought together over 8,000 miles by ham phone patch . . . a yachtsman asking his broker why he bought instead of selling! Yes, you can hear the world and the strange voices in it with a shortwave receiver!

DRAKE SPR-4 Communications receiver provides longwave and shortwave reception in 30 bands. Tuning dial may be read to one kilocycle. Mode switch permits reception of AM, SSB or c-w signals. Maximum sensitivity is provided by preselection stage. Signal strength is read on S-meter.

CHAPTER II

Shortwave Reception—The Easy Way

To obtain the best results from your shortwave receiver it is a good idea to have some working knowledge of what radio is, and how long distance signals are propagated. This chapter explains the phenomena of long distance signal reception and gives you an insight into the operation of your receiver. The fine skill of tuning and logging shortwave stations is discussed, together with hints that will help your reception.

What is radio? This invisible, intangible servant of man is the greatest wonder of the world. Scientists can scrawl lengthy formulae on paper to explain the theory of the airplane, the secrets of the A-bomb, and the mathematical concept of hyperbolic, warped space. But of the ultimate nature of the radio wave, they know nothing. A simple definition of a radio wave is *electrical energy that has escaped into space. Radio*, in the overall sense, is not a *thing*, such as a chair or a house, but is a way in which things behave. Its effects can be measured and predicted, and it can be generated and put to use by man. Beyond that, radio falls into the twilight world of electromagnetic radiation which man is trying desperately to penetrate and understand.

ELECTROMAGNETIC RADIATION

Every electrical circuit that carries alternating current radiates a certain amount of this energy into space in the form of *electromagnetic waves*. The amount of radiated energy is small when the waves are large, as in the case of the ordinary 60-cycle electric light wires in your house. As the frequency of alternation is raised and the wavelength is lowered a region is reached where the invisible field becomes of some use for long distance communication. This region is termed the *communications range of the electromagnetic spectrum* ("radio waves"). Increasing the frequency of alternation above the range of radio waves leads first into the *infra-red region*, then into *light waves, ultra-violet waves, X-rays*, and finally *cosmic*

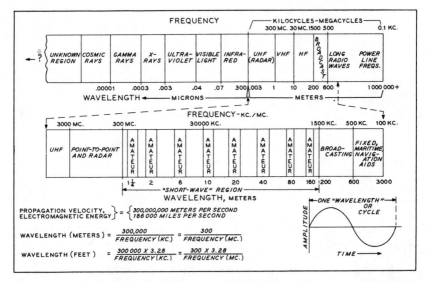

Fig. 1 Radio frequencies are but a small portion of the electromagnetic spectrum. As wavelength shortens, radio waves merge with infra-red waves. Waves may be described in terms of wavelength and frequency. The radio wave travels through space at a speed of 186,000 miles per second, or 300 million meters per second. The frequency, wavelength, and the speed of the radio wave are all related to one another as shown in the above equations. Use these equations to make conversions between frequency and meters!

rays. The whole gamut of radiation of all types falls neatly into place in the electromagnetic spectrum, as shown in Figure 1. Of great interest to the shortwave enthusiast is that portion of the spectrum falling between the higher limit of the broadcast band (1600 kc) and approximately 30,000 kc, for in this region extremely long distance radio communication takes place.

Before we examine this region more closely, let's pause a moment and examine some rather common terms that define the particular spot in the spectrum at which we may choose to tune our receiver. These terms are: *kilocycle*, *megacycle* and *meter*. Accompanying them are the terms *wavelength* and *frequency*. What do they mean?

WAVELENGTH AND FREQUENCY

A confusing situation exists in that any given radio signal may be described in terms of *frequency* (rate of change of alternation of the wave) or in terms of *wavelength* (physical length of one wave cycle). The radio wave (like all electromagnetic energy) travels through space at the speed of light which is about 186,000 miles per second, or 300 million meters per second. The meter is a unit of measure of the physical sciences and is approximately 3.28 feet in length. Because the radio wave occupies both time and space the wavelength and the frequency and the speed of light may all be packaged into a neat little formula that will translate wavelength into frequency and vice-versa, as shown in Figure 1.

As a quick mental exercise, let's assume a transmitter is operating on a frequency of 25,000 kilocycles (25 mc). By dividing the speed of light by the frequency, we find that the wavelength of the station is 12 meters. You will note that the conversion data of Figure 1 will work for meters and kilocycles, and meters and megacycles. Just be sure to keep track of your zeros, and all will come out well!

Radio Propagation

Although we cannot see the electromagnetic radiations leaving the transmitting antenna, instruments can measure and describe it, and theory and experiments can tell us what it does after it has left the antenna. Radio signals leaving the antenna are influenced by a number of factors, some of which may be controlled, and others which are beyond our power to control. We can control the angle and the direction taken by the signal as it escapes into space by making changes in the electrical characteristics of the antenna and by changing the height of the antenna above the surface of the ground, but after the wave has left the antenna system we are powerless to control it.

A portion of the radiated energy hugs the surface of the earth and is termed the *ground wave*. Commercial broadcasting stations make use of the ground wave, since it has proven to be a very reliable means of communicating over medium distances. Ground wave coverage in the broadcast band may range up to 500 miles, the coverage increasing as the frequency diminishes. Large portions of the earth may be covered by the ground wave at frequencies in the 100 to 200 kilocycle region. At the higher frequencies

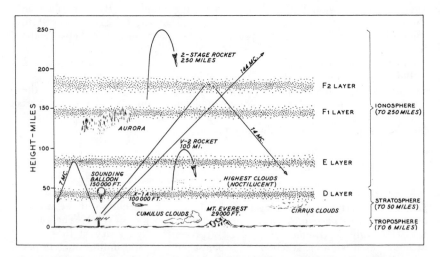

Fig. 2   The earth's atmosphere is composed of three layers, the lowest of which is the troposphere, or weather layer. The stratosphere (constant temperature zone) is next, extending to a height of about 40 miles. Above this is the ionosphere (ion layer) which is the region of reflection of radio signals.

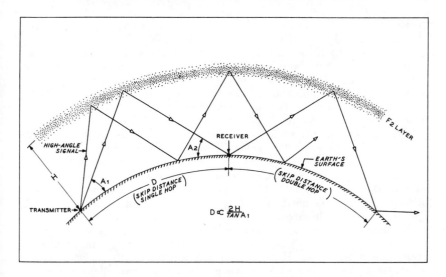

Fig. 3 Single hop transmission takes place up to distances of about 2500 miles. Beyond this the angle of radiation becomes too low to clear the earth, and radio signals must reach more distant areas by means of multiple-hop transmission. Silent zones (skip distance areas) between the hop points may be noted. Occasionally, the signal may reach a distant point by travelling the "long path," opposite in bearing to the great circle path by 180 degrees. Signals arriving over both long and short paths have bad echo and flutter.

(shorter wavelengths) the ground wave diminishes, dropping to a dozen miles or so in the vicinity of 10 mc. The ground wave does not again become useful until the VHF (Very High Frequency) region above 50 mc is reached. Ground wave propagation is used at VHF for television, FM, and other forms of propagation covering limited areas of high population density.

A second portion of the radiated energy is termed the *sky wave* which increases in effectivity as the frequency of operation is increased. First noted in the early "twenties," the sky wave permits communication at great distances that are not normally reached by the high frequency ground wave. An additional characteristic of the sky wave is that it skips over the earth, jumping large areas and then showing up once more beyond the area of *skip distance*.

After a good deal of head scratching, the savants decided that the sky wave type of propagation was brought about by an area of the upper atmosphere known as the *ionosphere* (Figure 2). This interesting region hovers between 60 and 150 miles above the surface of the earth and "bounces" high frequency radio signals back to earth that would otherwise be lost in outer space. In this region of the upper atmosphere, energy from the sun strikes particles of the air and ionizes them, releasing free electrons from the particles. The blanket of electrons formed by this action has the unique ability to reflect radio signals of certain frequencies back to the surface of our planet. Radio signals aimed at this invisible mirror are reflected back to earth, many thousands of miles away from the transmitter.

The degree of ionization and the height of the ionized layer changes from day to day, and from darkness to light, and the reflective ability of the layer varies with these changes. At times the layer is in fine fettle and reflects radio signals in robust fashion, and all is well. Often, the layer goes mildly beserk from the lashings of ultraviolet radiation emanating from the sun, and radio transmission via ionospheric skip "goes to pieces." Between these two extremes radio conditions vary from day to day, and from hour to hour, to the delight or the despair of the radio ham.

The reflective ability of the ionosphere is largely a function of the frequency of the radio signal, in general being best for the higher frequencies. However. as we progress in frequency much above 30 mc, the radio signals tend to pass through the ionized layer and do not return to the earth. This is a comforting thought to those who wish to talk to the moon, but it is not much help to the amateur wishing to talk to distant points on the earth by employing the higher radio frequencies.

The highest frequency reflected back to earth between two distant points may be termed the *maximum useable frequency* (MUF) for that particular transmission path. The MUF seems to be a function of the 11 year sunspot cycle, the highest values of MUF being recorded at peaks of the cycle.

IONOSPHERIC VARIATIONS

Nothing is still in nature. The earth, moon, and sun all change their positions with respect to one another and the electromagnetic radiations from the sun wax and wane. Short wave transmission conditions fluctuate

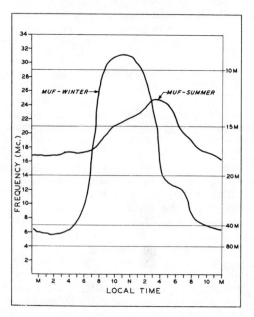

Fig. 4 The MUF for a typical east-west path during the low period of the sunspot cycle rarely peaks over 17 mc. At the top of the cycle the MUF may rise to 50 mc or more.

TREMENDOUS ANTENNAS and high power transmitters are used by major shortwave broadcasting stations to overcome vagaries of ionospheric transmission. Shown at right is technician making adjustments on transmitting tower of VOA relay base at Munich, Germany.

from day to day, and from hour to hour. Over the years, a study of propagation conditions has clarified the situation, permitting forecasts to be made in advance of coming radio conditions. Like the weather, however, the radio conditions often do not follow the "advice of the weatherman," but long term variations in propagation can be computed, and the picture of the never-ending fluctuations becomes clearer.

Strongly ionized layers of the atmosphere reflect radio waves of high frequency that would easily pass through weakly ionized layers. Thus propagation conditions are dependent upon the degree of ionization. Ionization decreases when the earth swings past the orbital range farthest from the sun, and radio conditions may be expected to deteriorate during these summer months. Because the axis of the earth is tilted from the perpendicular to its orbit the winter nights are long compared to the twilight hours of summertime. Both these properties have a profound effect upon shortwave radio conditions. The extended winter periods of darkness allow greater time for the various layers of the ionosphere to de-ionize and to pass larger chunks of the radio spectrum into space.

The effect of these fluctuations in the ionosphere set a maximum frequency limit of reception for a given path (MUF) which varies from season to season as shown in Figure 4. The MUF for an east-west path across the United States is shown for summer and winter conditions. During the long summer days when the earth is at the outermost reaches of its orbit, ionization of the upper air is weak, but relatively constant over a 24 hour period, and the MUF varies over a restricted range of frequencies. Communication is impossible on paths whose propagation figure lies above the maximum useable frequency, and the path gradually decreases in effectiveness as the operating frequency is decreased below the MUF.

The winter days bring the earth closer to the sun, increasing the level of ultra-violet radiation falling on the ionosphere. The long winter nights allow a longer period of de-ionization. As a consequence the MUF reacts in a more violent manner, dropping to low levels at night, and then increas-

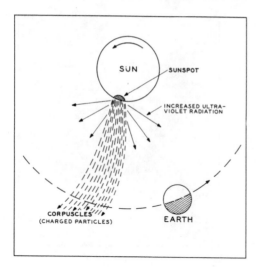

Fig. 5 Sunspot storm bombards earth with charged corpuscles creating ionospheric chaos. The MUF "radio dropout" is sometimes avoided by the earth passing ahead of corpuscular cloud.

ing to a maximum figure during the hours of the day. Thus, during a winter evening, a noticeable thinning out of stations will be apparent as the higher frequencies pass across the dial. Signals from these stations are passing through the ionosphere, escaping reflection to ears of listeners on earth.

At intermediate frequencies, communication may be supported between distant points almost 24 hours a day. This comes about when the frequency is close to the MUF. As shown in Figure 4, a transmitter operating on 16 mc could maintain communication over this particular path with the exception of a few questionable hours around 4 p.m., local time, when the MUF would be too high for good, reliable communication. Highly directional antennas and large power levels help the major shortwave broadcasting stations make the best of the situation when the qualities of the ionosphere are marginal. For the reader who is interested in pursuing this topic further, additional reference material is given at the end of the book. As a result of the undulations and changes in the radio mirror above the earth, shortwave reception does not occur on the steady, reliable basis we are accustomed to expect from broadcast band stations. The shortwave signal that breaks your eardrums may be a whisper in a few hours, and completely gone the next day. The station that can barely be heard at noon may be of overpowering strength at five p.m. This only adds to "the sport of the chase" and makes life more interesting to the avid shortwave listener!

During certain years the sun has large prominences on the surface that may be seen by looking at it through a piece of dark glass. These *sunspots* are of unknown origin, proof of violent agitation on and within the sun. Occasional huge solar flare-ups or *sunspot storms* are apparently connected with sharp increases in ultra-violet radiation and result in the emission of electrified particles or corpuscles which bombard the atmosphere of the earth. The increase in radiation from the sun is responsible for *sudden ionospheric disturbances* (SID's) while the corpuscular particles following at a

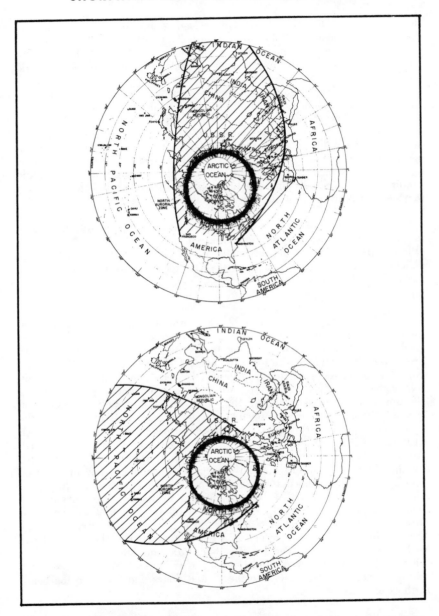

Fig. 6   An arctic projection showing the approximate location of the northern auroral zone. Cross-hatched area shows part of world that cannot be effectively reached by shortwave from U.S. due to shielding effect of the zone. Note that circuits from New York to Tangier and from San Francisco to Manila are not shielded by this zone. Below is shown the auroral shielding of transmissions from Tangier. Note that areas shielded from New York can be covered by relay station in Tangier. Same effect is true of relay base in Manila.

slower speed create delayed but longer lasting ionospheric and magnetic disturbances. The radio "black-out" is usually preceded by an increase in the MUF which may extend as high as 50 mc or so. The sunspots gradually build up in number and intensity over a regular period of about 11 years. During the peak of this cycle when the solar spots are most numerous, the MUF tends to average quite a bit higher than during periods of minimum sunspot activity. Thus radio conditions tend to become better during the peak of the 11 year sunspot cycle, even though the erratic bombardment of the earth by corpuscular emissions from the sun creates a greater number of radio "black-outs" during the same period. The present sunspot minimum occurred in the fall of 1976, and the cycle will gradually increase until a new maximum is reached about mid-1981. During the coming years, then, radio conditions will gradually improve and shortwave stations will begin to return to the higher portion of the HF spectrum, relatively vacant for the past decade.

In order to take advantage of the best propagation conditions, many international broadcasting stations transmit the same program on several different frequencies, taking advantage of the various different MUF's on difficult propagation paths, such as those near the North and South Poles.

The Auroral Zone

Covering the top of the globe like a crown lies the *auroral zone*, best known for the Aurora Borealis display in the heavens. A similar ring encircles the south pole, and is called the Aurora Australis. These displays are caused by visible ionization of clouds of charged particles thrown off from the sun. These particles are captured by the earth's magnetic field and follow the magnetic lines of force toward the geomagnetic poles, ionizing the upper atmosphere as they collide with its atoms. Radio transmission through the auroral zone is difficult since the efficiency of reflection of the ionosphere is low in this area. The ionized crown, therefore, blocks much of the Far East from effective radio reception and transmission from North America (Figure 6). Signals passing through this area are recognizable by their "auroral flutter" created by uneven reflection from the ionized layers of the area. The flutter may be so rapid that it renders the signal almost unintelligible. The *Voice of America* overcomes this difficulty by establishing auroral zone by-pass stations, or relay points that receive transmissions from the United States, boost them in signal strength, and relay them in the desired area of reception. *VOA* relay bases have been established in England, the German Federal Republic, Poro and Tinang (Philippines), Liberia, Tangier (Morocco) and Colombo (Sri Lanka). Most of these relay stations place strong signals into the United States and they may be heard with ease.

The Great Circle Route

Radio transmission between two points may be considered to follow the shortest path consistent with its reflections back and forth between the earth and the ionosphere. This path is known as the *great circle route*. This route is the shortest distance between two points on the surface of a

sphere, and usually appears as a curve on the regular maps. Great circle maps can be made for a specific locality, and several are shown at the rear of this Handbook for various areas of the United States. The great circle map is unusual in that a point of origin is chosen, and is placed at the center of the map. All directions radiate from this point, and a ruler laid from the center point to any other point on the map automatically traces a great circle route. Such a map is indespensible if it is desired to "aim" a directional antenna at some point thousands of miles away.

How To Tune A Shortwave Receiver

Oh, yes! There's an art to tuning a shortwave receiver! Even though the shortwave spectrum is broken into three or four bands on most sets, each band covers a tremendous amount of territory. Roaming at random across the dial may be easy, but it will not produce satisfactory results if you wish to hear distant stations! The first step in the right direction is to learn the purpose and function of all the knobs on the receiver. There is an ironic joke among receiver engineers that the instruction manual of the receiver is something to be thrown away with the packing box! They reveal that most of the letters written by receiver owners to the manufacturers ask questions that are fully covered in the receiver instruction manual. Read it! Practice tuning the receiver and use all the controls until you understand the many functions of the set.

When you have the "feel" of the receiver, try your first serious listening on the lowest frequency shortwave band. This covers the smallest segment of the spectrum. The signals are also stronger on this band and exhibit less fading than those higher in frequency. Tune the main frequency dial *slowly* and note how the stations come into audibility and fade out again. Note also that the stations are spaced closely together at some parts of the dial, and are farther apart at other places. Observe that each station occupies a much smaller fraction of the dial scale than does a broadcast station. Practice tuning in areas of interference and try separating one station from the other. A few minutes of practice in carefully tuning signals will pay big dividends.

Practically all shortwave receivers incorporate *automatic volume control* to reduce the effects of fading and auroral flutter. Always make sure that you use the a-v-c system when you listen to a telephone signal. Sometimes interference can be reduced by manipulation of the audio tone control. A high pitched hetrodyne between two adjacent stations can be reduced by turning the control towards bass reception. Under most circumstances the tone control should be advanced towards the treble end to allow faithful reproduction of speech, and to prevent the signal from sounding "boomy." Experienced shortwave listeners, incidentally, do most of their DX-chasing with earphones, rather than with the loudspeaker. Reception and comprehension are much better when external room noises are barred from the ear.

Next, turn the bandswitch to a high frequency band and practice tuning in a foreign broadcast station. Notice that it is harder to tune in a weak, fluttering signal than it is a strong, local one. Then too, it takes plenty of listening practice to enable you to understand words transmitted via a fluttery signal. Plenty of listening practice will boost your comprehension of weak and fluttery signals. It has been said that some amateurs interested in DX can place a pillow over their heads and hear two wires scratched together in Outer Mongolia! With plenty of practice, you can be that good, too!

C-W Reception

The next phase of listening is to master code (c-w) reception. C-w may be sent with a hand operated key, a semi-automatic key, or by tele-typewriter. The simplest form of code transmission is for the action of the key to turn the radio transmitter on and off. This does not make much of a difference in the receiver unless the *beat frequency oscillator* of the receiver is turned on. The b-f-o creates a beat note, or audible hetrodyne with the c-w signal, resulting in musical code signals that may be heard with ease. For best code reception the a-v-c system of the receiver should be turned off, and the r-f gain control is used to adjust the intensity of the signal. The audio gain control is turned *full on*, and the r-f gain control is adjusted for optimum signal strength. The beat oscillator control is adjusted to provide a pleasing tone or pitch to the c-w signal. Experiment with different settings of the b-f-o pitch control to find the one best suited to your taste. Always operate the receiver with the audio control full on and the r-f gain control retarded.

Single Sideband Reception

Many amateurs and commercial stations make use of single sideband

(SSB) transmission, wherein the radio carrier and one sideband are suppressed and only one sideband is transmitted. To the uninitiated, these signals bear a great resemblance to the squawking of a duck! It is necessary to restore the carrier to the signal before it becomes intelligible. The simplest method of carrier restoration is to use the b-f-o of the receiver as a local carrier. The receiver is set up as for c-w reception with the audio gain advanced and the r-f gain retarded. The b-f-o is *off*. The single sideband station is tuned in for maximum signal strength. Leaving the tuning dial alone, the b-f-o is turned on, and the pitch control of the b-f-o is *slowly* tuned back and forth. The squawking of the duck will gradually change pitch and start to resemble human speech. After the b-f-o control is adjusted for best intelligibility, the main tuning dial of the receiver may be retuned *very slightly* for best audio quality. Admittedly, this is a "cut-and-try" system of tuning a SSB signal, but unless your receiver has a calibrated b-f-o and you know which sideband the station is transmitting, this tuning sequence is as good as any other. Plenty of practice will do wonders to enable you to tune in SSB stations quickly and easily.

Many of the more expensive amateur and shortwave receivers have crystal controlled beat oscillators which are factory adjusted for proper CW and SSB reception. During the past few years, in fact, a majority of radio amateurs have switched to SSB from amplitude modulation (used by broadcast stations), and AM amateur transmissions are scarce indeed, except for some AM usage on 160 meters and the high frequency end of the 10 meter band. Many point-to-point circuits have shifted to SSB and the serious listener will soon learn to tune his receiver for proper reception of this mode, or he'll miss a lot of the action!

If you are buying a shortwave receiver, make sure it is properly equipped for SSB reception. Most modern receivers make use of a *product detector* for improved SSB reception. In this case, the mode switch on the panel may be labelled CW-AM-SSB, for three types of reception. Admittedly, reception of SSB is a struggle on a receiver not equipped for proper reception. So before you lay out your hard-earned money, make sure the receiver can properly receive SSB.

CHAPTER 3

How To Buy A Shortwave Receiver

If you are a Texas Oil Millionaire the best way to buy a good shortwave communications receiver is to shine the glare from your diamond stick-pin in the eye of the salesman in the radio store, gently tap the ashes from your five dollar seegar into his shirt pocket, and say, "Son, wrap up a dozen of your most expensive receivers. I'll take 'em all. One of 'em is bound to be good!"

Since there may be one or two readers who are not Texas Millionaires, the following points are offered in the hope that they may be of assistance to the prospective purchaser of a new receiver.

A receiver is pretty much like an automobile. The basic motor remains almost the same from year to year as the body style changes. Some developments are announced with a fanfare and then fade into oblivion—like "free wheeling." Like the automobile, receivers come in all sizes and prices, and some of them are good and some of them are not so good. And, like the automobile, the receiver grows old, starts to "burn oil" (blow out components), and is finally traded in on a new model. To carry the comparison to the final conclusion, there exist good buys in second hand receivers, just as can be found on the used car lot. This idea will be pursued later in this chapter. Right now, we'll lift the lid and peek into one of the brand new receivers and try and determine its true value.

The Skeleton

The stripped bones of a communication receiver are illustrated in Figure 1A. A converter stage, one i-f stage, a detector and audio stage, plus an output stage and a power supply make up the receiver. Such a device usually covers 550 kc to 30 mc in four tuning ranges. The receiver may be a portable job, running from batteries or it may be capable of operation either from batteries or the power line. It usually has a built-in loud speaker. The cost of such a set is fifty to eighty dollars. Despite the simplicity and the lack of an r-f stage, this "stripped down" receiver gives surprisingly good results, especially on the lower frequen-

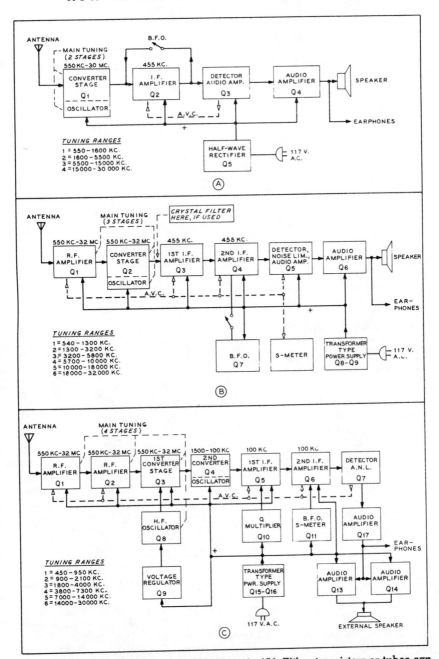

Fig. 1 "Basic" shortwave receiver is shown in (A). Either transistors or tubes can be used (Q1-Q5). Communication receiver with r-f stage, b-f-o and S-meter (B) uses nine tubes or transistors. Deluxe receiver with two r-f stages and all accessories (C) uses 17 tubes or transistors.

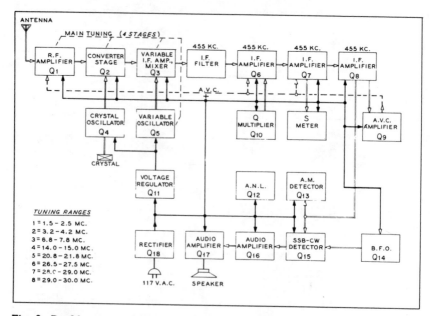

Fig. 2. Double conversion receiver employs high frequency i-f stage (Q3) to reduce image problem and low frequency second i-f amplifier (Q6-Q8) to obtain high order of selectivity. First conversion oscillator (Q4) is crystal controlled for highest frequency stability. Second oscillator (Q5) is tunable. Receiver employs 18 tubes or transistors.

cies below 10 Mc. Many a beginner has started listening on just such a set. The major defects with this simple design are that both the sensitivity and image rejection of the receiver suffer on the higher frequencies. Also, the receiver is prone to pick up power line noises that are coupled into the r-f circuits through the ac power supply. The set, however, is a good buy for the money, since many simple broadcast receivers cost as much.

The next higher cost receiver incorporates an r-f amplifier and a transformer-type power supply in the design. In addition, a noise limiter and a second i-f stage may be added. A true communications receiver results from these changes. Sensitivity, image rejection, and selectivity are greatly improved as compared to the "stripped down" set. The more expensive receivers in this category also add an S-meter and a crystal filter. The receiver has seven or eight tubes and costs from one hundred dollars to two hundred and fifty, depending upon the refinements incorporated in the circuitry.

The "Rolls Royce" of general coverage communications receivers is diagramed in Figure 1C. The receiver may have one or two r-f stages, and include double conversion. It will have a multi-position crystal filter, or perhaps a Q-multiplier. It will have plenty of audio, a regulated power supply, and an extremely rugged chassis. Critical circuits will be air-tuned and temperature compensated. A receiver of this class will cost from three hundred dollars to over six hundred dollars. It is strictly for the "pro-

TUNING ASSEMBLY of six band receiver uses multi-section variable capacitors to obtain proper tuning ratio. Main tuning gang is at left, and bandspread sections are at right. Coil catacomb is placed directly below the chassis.

fessional," since it requires a practiced hand to obtain all the benefits from its complicated circuitry. It may have as many as eighteen tubes (and almost as many knobs!).

A species to itself is the strictly "amateur communications receiver." A receiver of this type covers only the narrow segments of the spectrum occupied by the amateur bands, to the exclusion of the greater portion of the short wave region. It is designed to do a tough, specific job, and it does it well. It will not serve as a general receiver for casual listening, as it is designed and built for a particular type of service. For the serious amateur desirous of the best this type of receiver represents the ultimate in perfection. The block diagram of such a receiver is shown in Figure 2.

What to Look For When You Buy a New Receiver

The first thing to decide is "what brand of car" you wish to buy. In most cases, this decision is automatically made by the pocketbook. The real choice must be made between various receivers falling within the same price class. Excluding the basic receiver of Figure 1A, the following discussion applies to all other grades of receivers.

STABILITY—SENSITIVITY—SELECTIVITY

These three terms can be used to sum up the performance of any receiver. In order that you may evaluate the performance of your receiver, or one that you intend to purchase, an explanation of these terms is in order.

Stability

The electrical stability of the receiver is a function of the *thermal* stability and the *mechanical* stability. The thermal stability is a measure of the response of the receiver to changes in temperature. As the receiver warms up, the heat of the tubes and the power transformer gradually warm other components in the receiver. The tuned circuits are particularly sensitive to temperature changes. The thermal stability of the receiver is the ability of the receiver to stay tuned to a station after a short warm-up period. As the heat increases in the receiver cabinet, especially in the vicinity of the conversion oscillator, component values will change, causing the dial setting to slowly vary. This effect is known as *drift*, and can be very annoying if it is necessary to keep retuning a station for several minutes or even an hour after the receiver is first turned on. All receivers, except the most expensive have varying amounts of thermal drift, and it is well to check this drift before a new receiver is purchased.

Mechanical stability is a function of receiver design. The converter stage is especially sensitive to vibration in most receivers. Instability may be caused by loose components, poor tubes, or wires that move slightly when the receiver is vibrated. Many receivers having the speaker mounted in the case are prone to mechanical instability when the set is playing loudly. The vibrations of the speaker can lead to acoustic feedback, taking the form of a loud howl heard on strong signals. A well designed high frequency receiver will have a heavy case, with all parts firmly mounted to the chassis. Heavy leads will be employed in the r-f section of the receiver to reduce effects of mechanical vibration. Rubber shock mounts are employed in some cases to reduce vibration of the sensitive tuned circuits.

Sensitivity

Sensitivity is the ability of the receiver to receive weak stations over the inherent noise of the set. Of the three requirements for a good receiver, this one is the easiest for the manufacturer to meet. All but the most inexpensive receivers (having no r-f stage) have sufficient sensitivity and amplification to "pull in the weak ones." Generally speaking, the more tubes a receiver has, the greater gain it has. However, the amount of gain often does not really indicate just how sensitive the receiver really is. Some poor receivers having excessive gain merely amplify their own noise!

Selectivity

Selectivity is the ability of a receiver to reject unwanted stations. The true criteria of a good receiver is not what its receives, but what it rejects! This is the most critical requirement of the three, and the one where most receivers fall flat on their fuses. Because it is impossible to design a tuned circuit that will pass only one frequency, stations on either side of the wanted one will usually be heard, and will cause interference. Generally speaking again, the lower the intermediate frequency, and the more i-f stages, the better will be the selectivity of the receiver.

DRAKE SSR-1 shortwave receiver covers the broadcast band and HF bands continuously from 500 kc to 30 mc, and is a good example of medium-priced receiver. Dial readout is to 5 kc.

"Four Band" and "Six Band" Receivers

After hanging around the local radio store for a while, you will noice that some receivers cover the 550 kc to 30 mc spectrum in four ranges, while other receivers cover the same chunk of spectrum in six ranges. You can obtain this information merely by looking at the bandswitch of the receiver and noting the number of positions on it. Further cogitation upon this subject will reveal that—in general—the inexpensive receivers have four bands, and the more costly ones have six bands.

An obvious question is: Why are two different bandswitch systems used on shortwave receivers? Why don't all receivers either have four bands or six bands? How-come??? The answer to this query touches upon the economy of building a shortwave receiver in production quantities, and upon the desired signal-to-noise ratio of the receiver. It is easy to see that the least costly receiver would be one that had only one tuning range. This would do away with the bandswitch and the extra coils. The tuning dial of this receiver would cover 550 kc to 30 mc in one enormous range. If such a receiver was to be made, great economies would be gained, since a whole collection of expensive parts could be eliminated. A receiver of this type, unhappily, would be impractical for several reasons. First of all, the dial would tune over 24,450 kilocycles—almost twenty times as great a range as the whole broadcast band! Each shortwave station would occupy only an infinitely small speck on the dial. In order to tune a particular station, an expensive gear reduction system would have to be attached to the tuning capacitor of this receiver. In addition, the bearings of the capacitor would probably have to be hand-made and of the finest quality. The money saved by eliminating the bandswitch and extra coils would therefore be lost in the expensive dial mechanism necessary to tune the receiver.

Even if it were possible to manufacture an inexpensive high precision tuning dial, a second problem effectively eliminates the "single band" concept. The "fly in the ointment" centers around the action of the tuned circuits of the receiver when an excessive frequency span is desired. The coupling efficiency and impedance of the tuned circuits are in proportion to the ratio of inductance and capacitance required to tune the receiver to a given frequency. Other factors being equal, the sensitivity and signal-to-noise ratio of the receiver are highest when the largest value of tuning inductance and the smallest value of tuning capacity are used. The useable sensitivity of most receivers gradually drops off as the capacity of the tuning capacitor is increased. You will notice, therefore, that most amateur bands are placed at the high frequency end of the tuning dial of your receiver. Sensitivity and receiver performance is best at this tuning point, since the tuning capacitor gang is almost fully open. This deterioration is caused not only by a drop of tuned circuit impedance, but also by the fact that it becomes harder to keep all circuits properly aligned as the tuning capacity is varied. The greater the variance in capacity, the more complicated the alignment problem. This difficulty *could* be overcome as it is largely a problem of economics. If enough time and money was spent upon making precision tuning assemblies they might function exceedingly well over an enormous frequency range.

This whole philosophy of design, however, is headed in the wrong direction. Receivers have been built in the past which attempted to tune great segments of the shortwave spectrum without resorting to switching mechanisms. They proved to be expensive and unsatisfactory. The builders regretfully junked the idea of a single band receiver and turned their thoughts to systems of bandswitching.

The Tuning Ratio

The key to the problem seemed to be in obtaining acceptable results with a minimum number of tuning ranges. Experiments proved that a *tuning ratio* of about 2½ to 1 is a good compromise between economy and proper receiver operation. The tuning ratio is defined by the ratio of the of the highest tunable frequency on a given band to the lowest frequency. Thus, if a receiver tunes from 6mc to 18 mc, the tuning ratio is 18/6, or 3/1. If the receiver tunes from 6 mc to 12 mc, the tuning ratio is 12/6, or 2/1. The tuning ratio of the broadcast band is about 2½/1, so a variable capacity designed to tune over the broadcast frequencies will also work well covering the same tuning ratio on the shortwave frequencies. The use of a common capacitor for both shortwave and broadcast tuning is an economy that helps to allow receiver manufacturers to produce excellent, low cost shortwave receivers. Early receivers having this tuning ratio worked well over the shortwave spectrum, and it shortly became standard practice to hold close to this tuning ratio in most receivers. Only four different sets of coils are required to cover frequencies up to 30 mc or so with a 2½/1 tuning ratio, and the "four band" shortwave receiver became a reality.

The only disadvantages to the four band receiver were that the over-all sensitivity of the receiver tended to drop off at the low frequency end of the tuning range, and that alignment of the r-f circuitry became a bit critical. These difficulties could be overcome by improved design and assembly techniques of the four band coil assembly, or by the use of six bands instead of four. Both techniques are in use in modern receivers. The six band receiver covers the 550 kc to 30 mc range, with tuning ratios of 1.8/1. The sensitivity of the receiver is more constant over the smaller tuning range, and the alignment problems seem less severe. This tuning ratio

RADIO W7DET OF SEATTLE, WASHINGTON is outstanding example of home built equipment. Complete station fits atop a standard desk. Transmitter exciter is at left, with all-band variable frequency oscillator. Kilowatt all-band amplifier is at right. Control panel is at center, over Collins 75A-4 receiver. Across top are control equipment, auxiliary receiver, and clock.

is employed in some more expensive receivers. A receiver having a 1.8/1 tuning ratio costs more than one with a 2½/1 tuning ratio, since extra coils and bandswitch segments are required. The receiver performance, in general, is improved over the simpler "four bander", but at an increase in complexity and cost of the r-f circuitry.

It should be emphasized that either type of design works well. A good four band receiver will "run rings around" a poor six band receiver. You pay your money and you take your choice! As you well know, more Volkswagen autos than Lincoln Continentals are sold in the world! This is because the Volkswagen is less expensive than the Continental, and more people wish to own Volkswagens than Continentals. Either car will take you from one place to another. The one you buy depends upon your taste in motor cars and your pocketbook! If you are the famous Texas Oil Millionaire, you should buy the flashiest and most expensive six band receiver you can find. The rest of us will have to use our best judgment and pick and choose. In some instances the smaller car is better suited to the particular job than is the more expensive one. So it is with receivers. You can own a "Volkswagen" receiver or a "Continental" receiver. The choice is up to you.

How to Buy a Second Hand Receiver

The watchword for buying a second hand receiver is *caveat emptor*—let the buyer beware! You can pick up a dandy bargain in a second hand receiver, or you can get "caught with a lemon." Unfortunately in some cases the "lemon" looks good, and the bargain receiver may have a kicked-around appearance. The problem, then, is to be able to judge whether the receiver is good or bad before you pay your money for it!

So let's assume that you have a few bucks burning a hole in your wallet, and you want to buy a good short wave receiver. What to do? Should you pick up a brand new model and pay the full price, or should you buy a second hand receiver that someone else has used (perhaps not wisely but too well). This choice must be left up to the individual. As in the case of a second hand car, some people like 'em, and some people don't. If you are not adverse to the idea of a used receiver, the following hints will help you to pick out a good one.

First of all, you must *see* and *hear* the receiver before you buy it. Buying a receiver through a classified ad, or from a person in a distant town is a risky business. His idea of a "good, clean receiver" may be a lot different than yours is! Also, it is not easy to get any kind of a guarantee as to receiver operation in a situation like this. The best bet is to purchase the receiver from a store or from an individual that will give you an opportunity to try the receiver out before you buy it.

Following this advice, let's walk to the nearby radio distributor who has a whole room full of second hand receivers. Maybe we can find a good buy! After explaining to the salesman that we're shopping for a second hand receiver, he waves us into a small room with eight or ten receivers sitting on a long bench. "Help yourself, boys," he states. "Try 'em all, and let me know which one you want."

Armed with this permission, we look around the room. Not bad! The ten receivers represent eight different types, ranging in price from thirty to four hundred and fifty dollars. The first problem is to decide which one we are interested in. Having set a maximum limit of one hundred bucks, let's see what we can buy for that amount of money.

The salesman poked his head in the door. "Why don't you try that Super-Blooper 100 in the corner. Cost $278 new. You can have it for $140." A little rich for the blood, but a good place to start. Let's go down a "check list" and see how the receiver measures up to it.

Check List for a Used Receiver

1—Turn on the receiver and adjust it to the broadcast band. Listen to several broadcast stations. Make sure the S-meter (if any) works. It should "kick up" in a lively fashion. If it does not, or if the voice and music sounds muffled it is a warning that perhaps the automatic volume control section of the receiver is inoperative. Paper capacitors are often used in the a-v-c circuit, especially in receivers that are over five years old. These capacitors deteriorate with age, and the a-v-c action of the receiver gradually "goes to pot." Check the receiver for a-c hum. If it is excessive the filter capacitors are probably bad.

2—If the receiver seems to function well on the broadcast band, switch to each of the short wave bands in turn. You should be able to receive signals on each band if a good antenna is attached to the set. Notice if the background noise level is the same at each end of the dial. If the background noise level is greatest at the high frequency end of a band, it means that the alignment of the r-f circuitry for that particular band is not in adjustment.

3—Check the dial calibration of each band. Look for Standard Frequency Station WWV, broadcasting a musical tone and time-ticks on 2.5, 5, 10 and 15 megacycles. Observe how much error in dial reading occurs when the receiver is tuned to this station. Also, tune in the amateur bands and see if they occupy the proper place on the dial. If WWV shows up at the wrong place on the dial, don't waste your money calling the National Bureau of Standards to get them back on frequency, since the receiver is probably out of calibration.

4—If the receiver passes these tests, it is time to find out some of the more subtle points that differentiate a "good buy" from a "lemon." Tune in a strong station on the highest frequency band. Tune it in carefully and let the receiver sit at that dial setting for ten minutes or so. If the station gradually drifts out of tune, the receiver is temperature sensitive. Unfortunately, most receivers are more or less susceptible to this form of thermal drift, so you should not judge the receiver too harshly in this respect. However, the tuning should "settle down" and remain relatively constant 30 minutes or so after the receiver has been turned on. If a continual drift over a period of hours is noted, you had better pick out a different receiver!

5—The heart of the receiver is the band change switch. A good band change switch will last for hundreds of thousands of operations. Once in a while, a switch will be found with dirty or defective contacts. If you buy a receiver with a bad band change switch, you have "had it," since it is an expensive, major operation to replace it. To test the bandswitch, tune in a loud station on the highest frequency band. Carefully flip the bandswitch to the next lower frequency band, and then return it to the high frequency band. Can you still hear the original signal? No? Then turn the tuning dial and hunt for it. If the receiver requires retuning to the original signal when the band-switch has been turned and reset it is an indication of dirty or intermittent contacts in the bandswitch assembly.

This is a rather critical test, and many new, modern receivers right out of the packing case will not pass it. It is an expensive task to make a receiver assembly absolutely rigid, and the action of turning the band change switch can and does warp the chassis a small amount. This, in turn alters the configuration of the high frequency oscillator of the receiver, changing the dial setting a few kilocycles.

However, you can tell a lot about a used receiver from the band-switch. If the tuning returns to within a kilocycle or two of where it was before you made the test, and no excessive noise develops when you rock the band change switch back and forth on the contact, the switch is probably in acceptable shape. If the receiver breaks into loud noises when the bandswitch is turned, or the original signal is found several hundred kilocycles down the dial from its original position, the operation of the band change mechanism is open to suspicion.

6—Tune the receiver to the high frequency end of the highest frequency band. Advance the audio volume control and listen to the background noise of the receiver. Remove the antenna and see if there is a distinct drop in background noise, indicating the internal noise level of the set is less than the external atmospheric noise. If the receiver you are interested in has no r-f stage (that is, it has a two gang rather than a three gang tuning capacitor) you can forget this test, as the receiver is not sensitive enough to differentiate between the two types of noise. A good receiver should generate little noise when the antenna is removed.

7—The receiver should be checked for images. An *image*, as explained later in this Handbook, is a "repeat" signal from a loud station. That is, the station is heard at a second point on the dial. All receivers have images to a greater or lesser degree. You should make sure that the images of your prospective purchase are not excessive. If the receiver in question has no r-f stage, you might as well forget this test, since the image rejection of this type of receiver is very poor. That is one price you must pay in an economy receiver.

Tune the receiver to the 10 meter or 15 meter band and hunt for a strong signal. Note the frequency of the signal, then look higher or lower in frequency for a "repeat" or image signal. If the receiver is a single-conversion job having an intermediate frequency of 455 kc (ask the salesman about the intermediate frequency), the image signal

QSL CARDS GALORE! Voice of America received over 5300 reception reports from 60 countries in one month for the program "Panorama USA". Mrs. Helen MacKenzie, clerk of the English Language Branch of VOA adds mail to the pile.

will be either 910 kilocycles above or below the main signal. In most instances it will be lower in frequency than the test signal. The amount of attenuation of the image signal will give you a good idea of the image rejection of the receiver. If the receiver is properly aligned, there should be a definite difference in signal strength between the desired signal and the image. The greater the difference in strength, the better is the image rejection capabilities of the receiver. If there is little or no difference between the two signals, the receiver is either incapable of good image rejection, or it is out of alignment. In either case, the situation should be explored further before you "lay down your long green" for the receiver.

If two receivers of the same make and model are available for test, try both of them on the same signal and see which one has a better image rejection. Also, try receivers of different makes on the same signal. If you can hear WWV on 15 mc, it will make a good, steady signal for test purposes. You will require a good S9-plus signal to make this test, otherwise the image signal might be too weak to readily find.

8—Next, test the auxiliary controls to see if they are in good shape. Make sure the volume control and the r-f gain control are not noisy in operation. If the set has a crystal filter, be sure that it works. Check the tone control for operation. See that the pilot lamps light.

9—At this stage of the game, see if the owner of the set or the store salesman will remove the bottom plate of the receiver so you can examine the components. Look for charred spots on resistors that would indicate a short circuit at some time in the past. Examine the bypass capacitors. If they are tubular units, observe if the wax has been forced out of the ends of the capacitor, a sure sign of a leaky unit. Above all, see if the previous owner has incorporated any changes in the circuitry. If additional wiring or components that do not belong in the set are found, you had better "tread lightly," as you have no idea what unusual modifications the previous owner might have made.

10—Finally, make sure that you obtain an instruction book with the receiver. Attempting to align a receiver, or to trouble-hunt without the assistance of an instruction manual is like washing your feet with your socks on. You can do it, but it isn't fun!

So here you are with your second hand receiver picked out! Chances are it will not measure up to 100% on the above checkout list. If you are a "whiz" on receivers you can take it home and probably correct all the little complaints. If you are not an expert, or do not have the suitable equipment to repair and align the receiver you might be able to have the store align it for a small charge. Do not assume that if the receiver is up for sale it has been completely aligned and checked out. Many radio dealers take in old receivers in trade on new ones, and they consider the old ones to be "pains in the neck," since the mark-up on used receivers is small. As a consequence not much time is spent getting the old receiver into tip-top shape.

Finally, remember that "you get what you pay for." The very inexpensive receivers—the new ones—are little more than toys to begin with. When you buy a second hand one you are usually buying a pile of junk, as the receiver has no margin of safety to carry it through years of service. The older, more expensive receivers can be bought for 30% to 60% of their new price. Therein lies the bargains, for a good, old receiver is many times better than a new "cheapie." The only deterrent is that *you* are the one who has to find out which old receiver is good, and which is unsuitable. Here's hoping that this information will be of help to you.

Build Your Own Receiver?

The manly art of building your own receiver is almost as extinct as the famous dodo bird. A decade or so ago the home-made receiver was the rule rather than the exception. The main obstacle to receiver construction is that the total cost of parts required to build a good receiver is almost as high as the cost of a completely manufactured unit. In addition the "trade-in" value of a home-made receiver is just about zero. Nobody wants some other man's construction project. On the other hand, you can always recoup from 50% to 75% of the original cost of the manufactured receiver when you get ready to dispose of it. As with automobiles, some receivers depreciate faster than others. One of the most famous and expensive receivers depreciates only about 10% a year.

Of great interest to the enthusiast with a thin pocketbook is the fact that a commercial receiver may be bought through many radio stores on a time payment plan. Although interest is usually charged in such a case, the receiver can be enjoyed and used while you are paying for it. To carry home and use a $250 dollar receiver for a down payment of fifty dollars or so is a luxury that was impossible not many years ago.

CHAPTER 4

Know Your Receiver!

Are you a real "DX-hound" or merely a "knob tweaker"? Do you know how your receiver really works, or do you merely treat it as a piece of fine furniture? Look inside your receiver, and also remove the bottom plate. Do you see all those trimming capacitors and variable adjustments? When they are properly aligned your receiver will have ears like an Iroquois hunting party. When these adjustments are not properly made, your receiver will be as dead as a Scotch hamlet on Tag-Day. You can make minor adjustments to your receiver and make sure it is in tip-top condition if you know the purpose of all these little controls. The purpose of this chapter is to discuss these adjustments and how they affect receiver operation.

Any receiver, no matter how expensive, usually requires a checkup after it has been used for a period of time. You don't have to "change the oil every 1000 miles" as you do with your automobile, but you should have a periodic checkup to insure that your receiver will always perform to its greatest capability. The very minimum you should do is to clean the dust and dirt from the interior of the receiver every six months or so, and take the tubes out and check them in a good tube tester. A small ten-cent store paint brush will do a fine job of removing dust from the corners of the receiver chassis.

As soon as you get the receiver you should hook it up to your antenna and jot down notes concerning the performance in a notebook. You should log the error in dial calibration at each end of each band, make a note of the normal background noise, and a notation of the setting of the audio volume control for normal listening volume. If the sensitivity of the receiver should gradually decrease over a long period of time you would notice it as it would be necessary to gradually advance the setting of the volume control with the passage of time.

Someday the time will arrive when you decide that it is time to realign the stages of the receiver for maximum sensitivity and proper calibration.

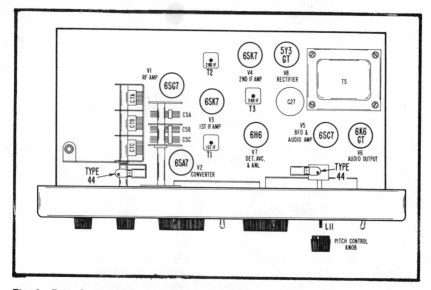

Fig. 1 Parts layout of typical shortwave receiver is logically arranged to permit shortest possible leads in radio frequency section. R-f amplifier and converter tube are placed adjacent to tuning capacitor, with bandswitch and coils directly below the chassis. The i-f amplifier is at the center.

You can do this the easy (and the expensive) way by taking the set back to the store from which it was purchased. You can save money and learn a lot, however, by aligning the receiver yourself.

Receiver Circuitry

Before you touch the interior of the receiver, it is a smart idea to familiarize yourself with the schematic of the receiver, and to correlate the part notations on the schematic with the actual components of the receiver. Remove the back and bottom of the receiver and examine the circuitry. Take a pencil and mark on the chassis near each tube or transistor the designation and function—i.e.: 2N2672, i-f amplifier, etc. That will help you to keep things in order while you trace out the circuit.

If your receiver is a true communications set, it will have a three gang tuning capacitor attached to the main dial, and perhaps a second three gang capacitor attached to the bandspread dial. In general, the following observations will apply to most all receivers of this class. First, the capacitor section nearest the main dial is the oscillator tuning capacitor. This unit determines the spot in the radio spectrum to which the receiver is tuned. The middle capacitor section is the mixer tuning capacitor, which tunes the signal circuit of the mixer stage. The rear capacitor section is the r-f amplifier tuning capacitor. When tubes are used it is quite easy to determine which stage is which, as tubes are designed for specific purposes (mixer tubes, amplifier tubes, detectors, etc.). The situation is more complex in solid state receivers where the designer has the choice of literally thousands of devices. The problem is further complicated in the imported receivers, as they employ transistors which do not conform to the standard nomenclature code used in the United States. In any event, the oscillator stage is usually closest to the front panel, the mixer stage being immediately behind it, and the r-f amplifier stage at the rear of the three gang tuning capacitor. A representative receiver layout for a medium priced receiver employing tubes is shown in Figure 1.

One important fact about a tube-type receiver is that the tubes can be removed and tested, whereas in many of the solid-state, transistorized receivers the devices are soldered directly to the circuit boards making the receiver much more difficult to service. Regardless of whether the receiver uses tubes or transistors, if it is well designed and properly built, it will function properly. In other words, don't base your decision to purchase a particular receiver on the fact that it uses tubes or transistors.

Most communication receivers employ one or two intermediate frequency stages, which commonly operate at a frequency of 455 kc. A tube-type receiver may use a 6BA6 or a 6SK7 in these stages. Again, the choice of transistors for this service is infinite.

The second detector and audio sections of the receiver vary greatly from one design to the next, and from one model to another of the very same manufacturer. In tube-type receivers, a 6AL5 is often used as a second detector,

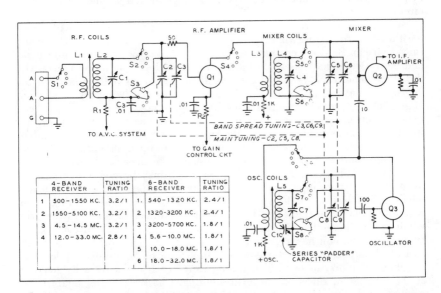

Fig. 2 The r-f circuitry of a typical shortwave receiver. Unused coils are shorted out by S3, S6 and S8. Devices Q1-Q3 may be tubes or transistors. Oscillator and mixer functions may be combined into one device in the less expensive receivers. R-f tracking of oscillator is accomplished by series "padder" capacitor C10 which is switched with the coils. This capacitor determines the rate of tuning of the oscillator, which is different from that of the r-f amplifier and mixer circuits.

a-v-c stage and noise limiter, followed by one or two stages of audio, using a 6AQ5 or 6V6. As before, the choice of transistors is wide.

The more expensive receivers may incorporate extra a-v-c tubes, S-meter tubes, and double conversion circuits to cloud the issue. Even so, armed with the schematic, and with the receiver upended before you, you should soon be able to pick out the major circuit components.

The Radio Frequency Section

You will note that the r-f coils mounted below deck are arranged around the bandswitch in such a manner that the leads from the coil to the switch, and from the switch to the transistor, or tube socket, are as short and direct as possible. They are usually made of very rigid wire.

Once you have determined which set of coils belongs to the oscillator, and which sets belong to the mixer and r-f amplifier respectively, you are ready to study the r-f circuitry more closely. The schematic of Figure 2 is a general circuit that is common to most receivers having an r-f stage. Compare it with the schematic of your receiver. Trace out the wiring between the switch assembly, the tuning capacitors, and the tubes on a separate piece of paper and compare it with Figure 2 and with the schematic in the instruction manual. Let's take each stage at a time and go over the circuit.

Most receivers cover the broadcast and shortwave range with four positions on the bandswitch. A few receivers cover the spectrum in six ranges. It can be deduced that the "six band" receivers require more coils and more switch contacts to do the job and therefore cost more money. On the other hand, each range covers less of the spectrum than is covered by any single range of the "four band" receiver, resulting in somewhat simpler alignment and adjustment problems. A discussion of the virtues of "six band" receivers as against "four band" receivers has been covered earlier in this Handbook. Since each of the three r-f circuits of the receiver has one set of coils for each band, the "four band" receiver should have a total of 12 coils, and the "six band" receiver should be the proud owner of not less than 18 coils. As seen in Figure 2, each coil may have several windings on it. The r-f stage input coil, L1-L2 has two windings. L1 is the antenna winding and has a small number of turns. L2 is the grid winding. You will notice that each input coil has a different number of turns on the grid winding. The highest frequency coil has only a few turns, and each lower frequency band coil has a greater number of turns. The coil for the broadcast band may have many turns wound in a *bank* or *honeycomb* style. It is possible, therefore, to tell which tuning range each coil covers by looking at the number of turns on the grid winding. Check each coil against the position of the band switch knob, and the position of the wiper arm of the switch.

It is common practice to short out the windings of the unused coils in each stage to prevent them from reacting with the active coils. The coil switch (S2-S3) will therefore have two decks. Deck S2 selects the proper coil, and deck S3 shorts out the other coils. For economy, these two decks may be mounted on opposite sides of one switch segment.

NBS CESIUM FREQUENCY STANDARD is used at station WWV to control frequency of all transmissions. Voice and code announcements are automatic. WWV and WWVH (Hawaii) are useful for alignment required by all shortwave receivers.

The mixer coils (L3-L4) are very similar to the r-f input coils, as they cover the same frequency range. Upon close examination, it can be observed that the primary winding (L3) has more turns upon it than does the corresponding primary winding (L1) of the input coil. This is necessary to achieve good signal transfer from the r-f tube to the mixer tube. In all probability, grid winding L2 of the input coil will be exactly the same as grid winding L4 of the mixer coil. Three separate switches are employed to choose the proper mixer coil: Deck S4 selects the plate coil for the r-f tube, deck S5 selects the proper grid coil for the mixer tube, and deck S6 shorts out the unused grid coils. These three decks may be mounted upon two switch segments. Occasionally, you will find a receiver where (by a burst of ingenuity) all three switches are mounted upon one segment! A veritable rat's nest of wires will lead to this one deck!

Bandspread Tuning

All modern short wave receivers employ *bandspread tuning* whereby a small portion of the high frequency spectrum may be spread over a large segment of the dial for ease of tuning and logging accuracy. The bandspread may be a mechanical type, using a gearing system which permits a slow rate of tuning with an auxiliary tuning knob. This corresponds to "low gear" in an automobile, where the rear wheels turn slower than normal at any given motor speed. In the case of the receiver, the tuning capacitor turns slower than normal for any given speed of rotation of the bandspread tuning knob. One dial and two tuning knobs may be employed, or a separate bandspread dial and tuning knob may be added to the receiver. In either case, only one three section tuning capacitor is used. This type of bandspread is commonly used in inexpensive receivers having no r-f stage. It is not costly and it works well.

More expensive receivers employ electrical bandspread which requires a second three gang tuning capacitor. This capacitor may be readily recognized since it will have only two or three plates per section. In some receivers it is incorporated as part of the main tuning capacitor. A separate dial and tuning knob is used to tune the bandspread capacitor. In Figure 2, the main tuning capacitor gang is C2-C5-C8, and the bandspread capacitor gang is C3-C6-C9. The bandspread dial is usually calibrated in kilocycles for each amateur band. In addition it often has a 0-100 degree calibration for general use at other portions of the short wave spectrum.

When electrical bandspread is not desired the bandspread dial is set so that its capacitor gang is at minimum capacity (plates unmeshed). When it is desired to use the bandspread dial, the main tuning dial is set to the *high frequency* side of the portion of the spectrum over which bandspread action is desired. The bandspread capacitor is then slowly meshed, adding circuit capacity and tuning the receiver lower in frequency. Thus all bandspread action normally starts from the high frequency end of the bandspread dial and progresses lower in frequency. Let's assume that you want to bandspread the 14 mc amateur band. The main tuning dial is set slightly above the high frequency end of the band, say to 14.4 mc with the bandspread dial set to its maximum indicated frequency (capacitor plates unmeshed). Tuning the bandspread dial will now cover the 14 mc band, starting at the high frequency end and advancing toward the low frequency (14.0 mc) end.

Padding Capacitors and Slug Tuned Coils

If a short wave receiver was precision-made by an electronic engineer who measured each component to insure its absolute accuracy, and who aligned the receiver with the most expensive and precise instruments, it would be a fine set, indeed. It would also cost about $10,000. It is a tribute to the receiver manufacturer that he can approach this stage of excellence on a production basis and yet sell the receiver for a modest sum. In order to do this, he has to have some means of compensating for the normal, slight variations inherent in all radio tubes and components. To insure that the tuned circuits of the receiver cover the range they are intended to, padding capacitors and slug tuned coils are employed, permitting close adjustment of the circuit parameters.

To begin with, the minimum amount of circuit capacity must be determined, for even with the main tuning capacitor and the bandspread capacitor set at zero (plates unmeshed) the wiring, components and tubes contribute a measureable amount of residual capacity that must be taken into account. This "bottom" capacity may wander over a wide range, and varies with make of tubes used, placement of parts, lengths of interconnecting leads, and slight tolerance variations in manufacture of the individual components. To establish a standard value of "bottom" or minimum capacity, small *padding capacitors* (C1, C4, C7, Figure 2) are added to each tuned circuit. In this manner, the manufacturer can adjust the padder and set the minimum capacity of the tuned circuits to a specific value without fuss or bother. Since the receiving antenna has a slight detuning effect upon the first r-f circuit of the receiver, the padding capacitor for this stage (C1) is often made adjustable from the panel of the set, permitting the r-f stage to be peaked to match the antenna in use.

Once the minimum circuit capacity has been established, the balance of the circuit must be adjusted to tune to the desired low frequency as read at the opposite end of the dial. The low frequency limit reached by the circuit is determined by the size of the tuning capacitor and the inductance of the coil. Since it is not easy to alter the maximum capacity of the tuning capacitor without physically bending or changing the plates, the logical solution is to vary the inductance of the coil. This can be done by moving a powdered iron slug up and down within the coil. Thus the correct alignment of the r-f stage at the high frequency end of the band is adjusted by means of the padding capacitor shunted across the coil, and the alignment of the stage at the low frequency end of the band is accomplished by varying the slug within the coil.

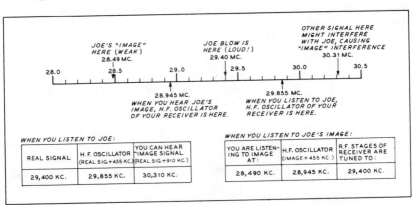

Fig. 3 Image situation becomes confusing at the higher frequencies where both signals may be audible. Above chart shows relation between fundamental and image signal when receiver conversion oscillator operates on the "high side" of incoming signal. Conditions are reversed for "low side" operation of the oscillator. Most receivers employ "low side" oscillator operation on all but the highest frequency band, where "high side" operation is occasionally used.

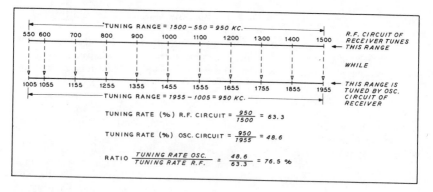

Fig. 4 Ratio of the tuning rate of h-f oscillator and r-f stages in superheterodyne receiver is different, although all stages tune through the same number of kilocycles. Shown above is relationship for broadcast band coverage of receiver employing 455 kc i-f amplifier. The tuning ratio is 76.5%.

Tracking the Tuned Circuits

As the receiver owner gaily tunes his receiver from one end of the dial to the other, he pays scant attention to the fact that the oscillator stage is racing along 455 kilocycles higher in frequency than that indicated on the receiver dial. When the receiver is tuned to 10,000 kilocycles, the oscillator is tuned to 10,455 kc. As discussed earlier in the receiver theory section, a superhet receiver tunes two frequencies at once, one higher in frequency than the conversion oscillator and one lower in frequency. The purpose of the r-f and mixer coils is to select the chosen frequency and reject the unwanted one. For ease of alignment, the signal frequency *lower* than the conversion oscillator frequency is normally used. In this case, the unwanted *image signal* should appear at a dial reading approximately 910 kilocycles *below* that of the real signal. The image signal should be considerably weaker than the desired signal *if* the r-f and mixer tuned circuits are properly aligned. For an example, let's assume local amateur Joe Blow is transmitting on 29.4 mc. The image of his signal should be heard 910 kilocycles lower, or at 28.49 mc. If Joe's image signal is louder than his real signal, it indicates one of two things: either the r-f circuits of the receiver are incorrectly tuned to the image signal, or the local oscillator of the receiver is operating on the "low" side of the signal. The receiver instruction manual will tell you which side of the signal is the correct place for the oscillator stage. Look at Figure 3. It summarizes this confusing situation and can help you keep things in order.

As you might guess, making the local oscillator maintain a respectful separation of 455 kilocycles from the received signal is "not all beer and skittles" (as they say in the old country). Some pretty fancy tricks must be employed in the receiver to maintain accurate alignment. Just consider the problem: To cover the broadcast band, the r-f and mixer stages must tune from 550 kilocycles to 1500 kilocycles. At the same time the oscillator stage must tune from 1005 kilocycles to 1955 kilocycles, always maintaining

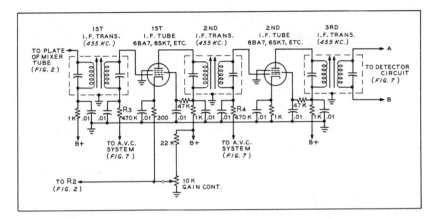

Fig. 5 Tube-type i-f amplifier. Signal from mixer stage is at constant frequency of 455 kc, regardless of frequency of reception. The greater part of receiver gain is obtained in the i-f amplifier. I-f transformers are aligned by adjustable powder-iron cores. I-f gain may reach 10,000.

the 455 kilocycle difference in frequency. This means that while the r-f and mixer stages are tuning *through a range of 950 kilocycles, the oscillator must tune through the same 950 kilocycle range.* (Watch out, now! Here comes the "joker"!) *The two tuning ranges expressed as a percentage of the highest frequency in each range are different!* The r-f and mixer percentage figure is 63.3, and the oscillator percentage figure is 48.8. Starting from the high frequency end of the dial, the r-f stages tune 63.3% lower in frequency, while at the same time the oscillator only tunes 48.8% lower in frequency. Therefore the *oscillator tuning rate* must be *slower* than that of the r-f stages because it covers a smaller percentage range. In this particular case, the *tuning rate* of the oscillator is only 76.5% as great as the tuning rate of the r-f and mixer stages. This is summarized in Figure 4.

The result of this complex situation is that the oscillator circuit must be modified in order to decrease the tuning rate. This may be accomplished in several ways. The most common way is to decrease the inductance of the oscillator coil, or the capacitance of the tuning capacity by the insertion of a *series padder* (See C10, Figure 1). Adjustment of the series padding capacitor will vary the rate of tuning of the oscillator.

If you will examine one of the inexpensive tube-type or transistor broadcast receivers, you will note that no series padding capacitor is used in the oscillator stage. Rather, the variable plates of the oscillator tuning capacitor are cut to a different shape and size than those of the r-f section. This stunt can only be done in a receiver that covers a single tuning range, such as the broadcast band (540-1600 kc).

Summary: The high frequency oscillator must always be detuned to the high side of the signal frequency by an amount equal to the intermediate frequency. Since the percentage tuning rate of the oscillator is now less than the percentage tuning rate of the r-f circuits, a series capacitor must be added to the oscillator circuit to insure proper tracking between the stages.

The Intermediate Frequency Amplifier

The output of the mixer tube of a shortwave receiver usually falls in the region of 455 kc (with the exception of double conversion receivers). The greater part of the receiver gain and selectivity is obtained by the amplifying stages working at this frequency. The more expensive receivers having two stages of i-f amplification will naturally have better gain and selectivity than those receivers having only one stage. A typical two stage i-f amplifier is shown in Figure 5. Note that a single stage amplifier has two i-f transformers, and a two stage amplifier has three transformers. The best i-f transformers have fixed padding capacitors and powdered iron slug cores that are adjustable. The less expensive transformers have no slug, and the padding capacitors are variable mica units. Such transformers are susceptible to small tuning changes caused by variations in heat and humidity, and by deposits of dust in the mica capacitors.

All the transformers in the "i-f strip" are tuned to the same intermediate frequency of 455 kc. Each transformer has the property of accepting a narrow band of frequencies and rejecting all others. The better the transformers, and the more of them, the narrower is the passband of the receiver as shown in Figure 6. Selectivity, like all good things in life, cost money!

The Detector and A-V-C System

The next block of components to consider make up the detector and a-v-c system. Receiver manufacturers have as many different circuits to do these jobs as Carter has pills, and it is impossible to cover them all. However, they all have many points in common and a representative circuit is shown in Figure 7. The detector element may be a vacuum tube diode, such as a 6AL5 or a section of a 6AV6. Modern receivers use a semiconductor which

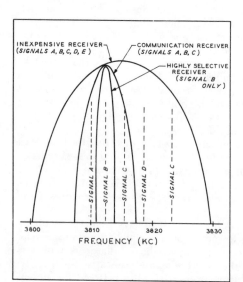

Fig. 6   Selectivity of the receiver is function of design of transformers in the intermediate frequency amplifier. To reduce inter-channel interference, good communication receiver must have passband less than 5 kc wide.

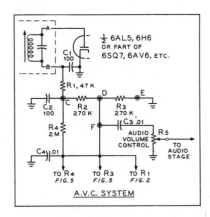

Fig. 7 Automatic volume control circuit reduces atmospheric effects on received signal, and prevents loud stations from 'blasting" the receiver. Speaker volume is held constant by varying gain of the r-f and i-f stages in proportion to strength of received signal. Control voltage is obtained in the detector of receiver directly from the incoming radio signal.

rectifies the signal as explained earlier in this Handbook. The rectified signal is passed through an r-f filter (C1-R1-C2-R2) and through audio coupling capacitor C3 to the volume control, R5. A portion of the rectified signal is passed through a second filter (C4-R4) having a relatively long time constant which washes out the modulation on the signal, leaving a voltage that is proportional only to the carrier strength of the signal. This voltage is returned to the grid circuits of the r-f and i-f stages to control their gain. The greater amount of a-v-c voltage that is developed across C4-R4, the greater the amount of bias voltage that is applied to the a-v-c controlled tubes in the receiver. By a proper choice of circuit constants, the audio level of the receiver may be held constant for signal strength ratios of 10,000 to one.

The Noise Limiter

The purpose of a noise limiter in a shortwave receiver is to protect the eardrums of the listener from loud bursts of static, and also to reduce the racket produced by man-made sources. A simple diode limiter that removes the noise "peaks" from the signal is shown in Figure 8. Variations of this

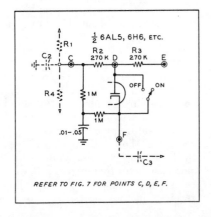

Fig. 8 Automatic noise limiter can easily be added to shortwave set to reduce static crashes and automotive ignition noise, which is particularly bothersome at the higher frequencies. "Popping" ignition noise is cut out of radio signal by action of diode tube. Five components and tube are all that are required to add noise limiter to most shortwave receivers.

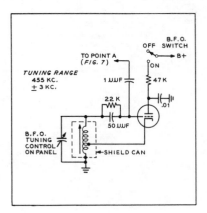

Fig. 9 Beat frequency oscillator is required for c-w and SSB reception. This circuit produces weak signal in i-f amplifier that is slightly detuned from incoming signal. The resulting "beat" or heterodyne makes code signal audible.

circuit are included in almost all receivers above the economy class. Operation of the device is automatic, since the bias for the noise rectifier is derived from the rectified signal appearing in the second detector circuit. When a loud noise pulse comes along the diode ceases to conduct, thus momentarily disconnecting the audio portion of the receiver from the detector. The simplicity of the device is apparent when it is seen that only four additional components need be added to the receiver to make the limiter! More complex limiters employing several tubes are employed in the larger receivers to provide better suppression of man-made interference.

Audio Stages, B-F-O, and Power Supply

The remainder of the receiver is very straightforward. The audio section may employ one or two pentode tubes in the output stage, along with a small audio amplifying stage. It is interesting to note that the less expensive receivers incorporate the speaker in the receiver cabinet, while the more elaborate receivers have the speaker contained in a separate box. It is a good idea to separate the receiver and speaker by a few feet, since the sound waves from the speaker can actually cause the wiring of the receiver to vibrate ever so slightly. This is of no concern on the broadcast band, and no great worry throughout most of the shortwave spectrum. However, in the vicinity of 15 mc to 30 mc the minute vibration of the r-f leads in the receiver can set up a weird feedback effect that will produce a loud howl in the speaker and a ringing noise that is most annoying and mystifying. The more pretentious receiver helps to solve this acoustical problem by the removal of the loud speaker from the receiver cabinet. Please don't spoil the cure by placing your loudspeaker atop the receiver! You are just asking for trouble at the higher frequencies!

The beat frequency oscillator (b-f-o) is a standard adjunct to all short-wave receivers. Many tube or transistor types can be used in this stage. The coil of the b-f-o is usually housed in a can similar to an i-f transformer. The b-f-o is a small oscillator that operates at, or near, the intermediate frequency of the receiver. The frequency of the oscillator may be adjusted from the panel of the receiver in most instances. For c-w reception, the b-f-o must be slightly

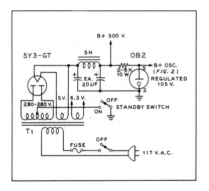

Fig. 10 Transformer-type power supply is standard equipment in communications receiver. High frequency oscillator voltage may be regulated by gas-filled control tube to achieve greatest frequency stability and immunity to line voltage fluctuations. Supply is fused for safety.

detuned from the intermediate frequency, it will create a beat note or hetrodyne with the signal in the i-f circuit. This is quite a nuisance for phone reception, but a tremendous help when receiving c-w signals and single-sideband stations. A typical triode b-f-o circuit is shown in Figure 9. In passing, it should be noted that the a-v-c system of the receiver must be disabled when the b-f-o is in use, or else the b-f-o signal would control the a-v-c voltage and desensitize the receiver. Most receivers couple the b-f-o and a-v-c switch together so that when the b-f-o is turned on the a-v-c system is shorted to ground, as shown in the schematic.

The power supply of the average short wave receiver is a rather unimaginative device. Ninety-nine times out of one hundred it consists of a capacitor input filter system (Figure 10). The better receivers incorporate an additional voltage regulator (tube or zener diode) which is used to insure a stable voltage is applied to the high frequency oscillator. In tube-type receivers, a 5Y3 is commonly used as the rectifier.

Miscellaneous Receiver Controls

A few other knobs decorate the panel of the shortwave receiver. The B-plus voltage may be interrupted by a *standby switch*, rendering the receiver inoperative during periods of transmission of a nearby transmitter. A potentiometer in the cathode circuit of the r-f tube may be used to reduce the r-f gain of the receiver for c-w and single-sideband reception.

SPURIOUS RESPONSES

The true criteria of a good receiver is *not* what it receives, but what it *rejects!* You can hear a lot of DX on most any old "clunker" of a receiver, but you will also hear a lot of spurious signals that are not supposed to be there! Since it is prohibitively expensive to design a tuned circuit that will pass only *one* frequency, stations on either side of the wanted one will usually be heard, and will cause interference. In addition, image response and "birdies" will place signals on your dial that you wish weren't there!

The image problem is discussed later in the Handbook, and we can examine the birdie problem right now.

Any superhetrodyne receiver can have spurious responses at frequencies other than the one to which the receiver is tuned. The response to the unwanted signal will depend upon the susceptibility of the receiver to spurious signals, and the actual strength of the radio signal that happens to be situated where the receiver has a "weakness." If you are in the middle of the Sahara desert with no radio stations within a thousand miles of you, the spurious responses of your receiver would cause you little worry. If you are in the center of a large city with amateurs, broadcast stations, police radios, ship-to-shore stations and countless others on all sides of you, it would be wise to give pause to this important problem. If your receiver has a tendency to respond to signals at unwanted frequencies you might hear the local broadcasting station in the middle of the 80 meter ham band, or the nearby police radio station squarely on top of the BBC in the 31 meter band. If you have never heard a birdie, you might just place a good, long antenna (200 feet or so) on your receiver and listen to the 160 meter region. Chances are—if you are located near a big city—you will hear a jumble of broadcast stations that are not really there. The spurious responses of your receiver magically produces them. If you shorten your antenna and decrease the signal pickup, the spurious responses will drop in strength and may even vanish.

There's not much you can do to the receiver to drop the level of spurious susceptibility. It's a sort of a built-in factor, and you are stuck with it. Some of the newer r-f tubes, such as the 6DC6 and the 6BZ6 are especially designed to cope with this problem. About the best thing to do is to place additional selectivity *ahead* of the receiver to reduce the level of the unwanted signals reaching the r-f circuits of the receiver. Transistorized receivers, especially the less expensive ones, have poor overload capability and may become completely inoperative in the presence of a strong signal.

Selectivity Aids for the Communication Receiver

Three items are in use today that help to obtain optimum selectivity in the communications receiver. They are the crystal filter, the Q-multiplier, and the mechanical filter. In each case, the idea is to narrow the bandwidth of the receiver, permitting the reception of only one station at a time. This function is accomplished in the fixed-tuned intermediate frequency amplifier stages.

The Crystal Filter

The crystal filter is a sharply tuned stage employing a resonant circuit made of a piece of critically ground quartz. The quartz crystal is tuned to the frequency of the i-f amplifier, and acts as a signal "gate," permitting the intermediate frequency to pass, and rejecting those frequencies on either side. The crystal filter is extremely effective for c-w reception, but does not perform nearly as well for phone reception. The crystal filter allows a high degree of rejection at *one* chosen frequency. By the use of a variable rejection control, a loud unwanted hetrodyne may be almost eliminated.

COLLINS MECHANICAL FILTER offers ultimate in receiver selectivity. This unit is a selective electro-mechanical device designed to operate in the intermediate frequency circuit of the receiver. It provides a passband having very high rejection properties to adjacent signals, as illustrated in Figure 6. The bandwidth of the mechanical filter is fixed, and different filters must be switched in and out of the circuit to permit various degrees of selectivity to be used. Collins 75A-4 receiver incorporates filter switch having three positions for 6 kc, 2.8 kc, and 500 cycle bandwith filters. The 500 cycle filter is used for c-w operation.

The Q-Multiplier

The Q-multiplier is a relatively new device for increasing the selectivity of a receiver. Electronically speaking, this circuit increases the "Q" (or figure of merit) of a coil in the i-f amplifier to the point where the tuned circuit employing this coil will pass only a narrow band of frequencies. This is by far the simplest and most inexpensive means that the Novice can employ to increase the selectivity of his receiver, therefore a Q-multiplier is described in detail in the chapter devoted to Novice aids. The Q-multiplier may be used for either phone or c-w reception.

The Mechanical Filter

The Collins mechanical filter employs small resonant metal discs that are tuned to the i-f frequency of the receiver. The passband of the mechanical filter is excellent, and it is by far the best (and most expensive) device for obtaining maximum receiver selectivity. The passband of this type of filter is fixed, and various models of the filter allow the use of different passbands for phone or c-w reception. Its characteristic broad flat-top and steep sided response curve make it a pleasure to copy phone or c-w even under the worst QRM conditions.

The unusual Barlow-Wadley XCR-30 portable receiver tunes between 500 kHz and 30 MHz on two drum dials without bandswitching. It employs 14 transistors and one IC in a 4-conversion circuit to get continuous frequency coverage. The receiver is made in South Africa and is imported into the U.S. by a few distributors.

CONVERTERS

There is one form of "receiver" that has not yet been discussed, and that is the *converter*. A converter is a device that will extend the tuning range of a receiver. Take your home radio for example: If you desired to listen to short wave signals, you could build a converter similar to those shown in this Handbook which would extend the tuning range of the b-c set up into the short wave bands. Admittedly, the combination would not make a very good communications receiver, but it would work.

Converters are divided into two groups, tunable and fixed-tuned types. Both have decided advantages and disadvantages that make one type preferable to the other for certain applications.

Either type of converter may be used in conjunction with an inexpensive shortwave receiver to improve reception at the higher frequencies. As an example, most of the inexpensive communications receivers will not perform to a high degree on the 10 meter band (28-29.7 mc). It is possible to build a converter that will "beat" the 10 meter signals down to a lower frequency at which the receiver will be more sensitive. Converters are also used to an advantage in conjunction with an automobile receiver to facilitate mobile operation of an amateur station.

The converter, in effect, is comparable to the "front end" of a communication receiver. The receiver to which the converter is attached serves as the i-f amplifier and detector stages for the r-f circuits of the converter.

A block diagram of a typical fixed-tuned converter is shown in Figure 11 The r-f amplifier section is adjusted so that it will amplify a band of frequencies between 50 and 54 mc. The conversion oscillator is crystal controlled at 43 mc. Note that the conversion frequency is fixed, and cannot be changed unless a new crystal is inserted in the oscillator. Any signals

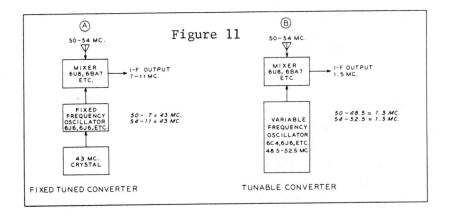

Figure 11

FIXED TUNED CONVERTER

TUNABLE CONVERTER

in the 50-54 mc range are mixed with the 43 mc oscillator signal in the 6U8 mixer tube. The i-f frequency range for reception across the six meter band is the difference in frequency between the tuning range and the conversion oscillator frequency. In this case, the i-f range is 7 mc to 11 mc. If the converter is attached to a communication receiver capable of tuning this frequency range, signals in the 50-54 mc range may be received. Note that the r-f stage of the receiver serves as a tunable i-f stage for the converter. The converter-receiver combination actually has two i-f channels, and is called a *double conversion receiver*. With a fixed-tuned converter, all tuning is done with the main tuning dial of the receiver. The converter can be tucked out of the way and left un-attended for long periods of time. Another advantage is that the crystal controlled conversion oscillator in the converter contributes negligible drift to the 50 mc signals. On the debit side of the ledger, this type of converter has lower gain than the tunable type, because the r-f stages must be adjusted to cover the complete band of frequencies to be received. The broad-band r-f stage will sometimes let signals get through it which are unwanted. These are known as *spurious signals*. In spite of this drawback, this type of converter is unanimously favored over the tunable converter for high frequency reception.

Figure 11 shows a typical tunable converter diagram. The oscillator section of this converter, unlike the crystal controlled model, can be changed in frequency by means of the main tuning dial. When used with an automobile radio, the i-f channel of the converter is 1500 kc. The car radio is tuned to that frequency, and the conversion oscillator of the converter always operates 1500 kc away from the received signal. A fixed intermediate frequency is used, and all tuning is accomplished at the converter. This type of converter features good gain, good selectivity, and good spurious signal rejection because all the r-f tuned circuits are sharply resonant at the incoming signal frequency. The disadvantages of this type of converter are the large size (because of the bulky tuning capacitor), thermal drift (because of the heating of the oscillator components) and relatively poor mechanical stability, especially in an automobile. In most cases, it is usually not as handy to tune the converter as it would be to tune the receiver. However, this type of converter is by far the most popular type for mobile reception.

CHAPTER V

Receiver Alignment—
How to Find and Catch Microvolts

Have you ever removed the covers to your receiver and poked around the insides? Have you ever adjusted the trimmers to improve reception? If you have, you are a proud member of a minority of listeners. Most SWLs shy away from the "innards" of the receiver as if there was a flame-thrower within, waiting to roast them to a crisp.

We take you on the hunt of the elusive microvolt and show you how it may be captured and tamed for better reception. Study and understand your receiver service manual and don't void the comprehensive warranty. With that caution in mind, take your alignment tool in hand, and away we go!

Inside your receiver are a multitude of small adjustment points called *trimmers*. These vernier adjustments control the sensitivity, selectivity, image rejection, and dial calibration of your set. If these adjustments are in perfect alignment, the receiver will perform to the best of its ability. When they are "out of whack" the receiver is subject to image interference, and it may become insensitive to all but the loudest signals, or the dial calibration may go awry.

The purpose of the trimmers is to insure that all the r-f circuits track perfectly as you tune the dial of your receiver. They compensate for slight variations inherent in the components and tubes of the receiver, and permit the tuned circuits to be placed "on the nose" before the receiver is sold.

Why worry about these adjustments? "If my receiver is new, haven't all these little jiggers and plungers been properly set by the manufacturer?", you ask. Well, perhaps not. Remember that your receiver is built and aligned on a production basis. The alignment is not done by an engineer, but rather by a technician trained for the job, who may or may not know anything about radio receivers in general, or shortwave reception! Perhaps the technician had a fight with his wife the night before, or perhaps came to work with a bad headache, or is worrying about the race for the pennant in the National League. Is he going to worry about the *precise* alignment of the particular receiver that you might chance to buy? Don't be silly. He will do

Fig. 1 Rear view of transistorized shortwave receiver showing placement of the major components. Most of the r-f circuitry is mounted on two large printed circuit boards. Power transformer and "loopstick" antenna for broadcast reception are at front of photograph. R-f circuits and trimmer capacitors are on left-hand circuit board, adjacent to main 3-gang tuning capacitor. Bandspread capacitor is immediately to the right, with the i-f and audio board at the far end of the chassis.

his best, and if the alignment job passes the minimum specifications demanded by the manufacturer, he will be satisfied. After the receiver leaves the factory it is trundled about in a box and jolted around at the mercy of the shipping crew and the not-so-tender hands of the freight carrier. The many uninterested hands pass the set along until it arrives at your house, ready to play. You take your chance on alignment accuracy, and hope for the best!

Let's look again at your receiver after you have had it for a year or so. The tubes and parts have aged and their electrical characteristics have changed a bit. Minute dust and dirt particles have sifted into the coils, capacitors, and switches of the tuned circuits. As a result, the important selectivity and sensitivity adjustments have slowly deteriorated over the months—so slowly that you have not noted the change. But your DX-bloodhound has gradually turned into a mongrel, and you are listening to all the stations through a thick veil of mis-alignment. You won't notice this gradual deterioration on a broadcast receiver tuned to a 50 kilowatt station a few miles away, but the change is deadly in the shortwave spectrum where the receiver is dealing with signals of microvolt intensity.

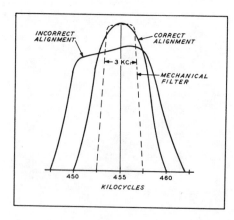

Fig. 2   Selectivity and gain of the receiver are determined by the i-f amplifier. The correctly aligned amplifier has symmetrical curve with rounded shoulders. A poor alignment job will result in lop-sided curve with tilted top. Ideal response curve is shown by dotted line. Mechanical filter produces response curve with relatively flat top and steep sides.

Let's Tweak An Adjustment—Just For Fun

Open the instruction book of your receiver and find the *Service and Alignment section*. Read it through and study the diagrams and alignment information. Particularly note the section dealing with alignment of the intermediate frequency (i-f) amplifier. Open the lid of your receiver and find the i-f transformers and tubes. Note that each transformer has one or two trimmers on it. The trimmers may be located on the top or the side of the transformers. If only one trimmer is on the top, the chances are that the second one is on the under-side of the transformer, and may be adjusted from the bottom of the set. These trimmers should be adjusted with the aid of an insulated screwdriver for two very important reasons. First, the trimmers may be "hot" with high voltage. If you touch them with the metal blade of a screwdriver you *might* get an unnerving and nasty shock. Second, the metal of the screwdriver might detune the circuit, causing a maladjustment in tuning. Many varieties of alignment tools are available in the large radio stores for less than a dollar. The *ICA #6192* alignment tool should do the trick for you.

The layout of a typical i-f amplifier is shown in Figure 1. Each stage is tuned by means of compression-type mica capacitors placed across each winding of the transformers, or by adjustable powdered iron slugs placed within the windings. The heads of these trimmers may be easily turned with the blade of the alignment tool with no danger of shock or misalignment.

Regardless of the frequency to which the receiver is tuned, the conversion process of the mixer stage changes the frequency of the signal down to the intermediate frequency, which is usually in the neighborhood of 455 kilocycles. This frequency is used, since it is possible to achieve more gain and selectivity per stage at a low frequency than at any frequency in the broadcast or shortwave spectrum. This is why almost all intermediate frequency amplifiers of modern receivers are tuned to some spot in the 200 kc to 500 kc frequency range. Selectivity and gain go hand-in-hand with inexpensive components and ease of adjustment. All i-f transformers can be tuned over a very narrow range, and they should be tuned to the single

intermediate frequency of the receiver by adjusting the trimmers mounted
on the transformers. If one transformer of an amplifier is tuned to 450 kc,
and another one is tuned to 457 kc, the response curve of the amplifier
will look like curve B of Figure 2. Sad, isn't it?

A combination of pentode tubes and high gain i-f transformers may
provide a signal gain as great as 10,000. In addition, the selective circuits
of the i-f transformers reject signals off the resonant frequency, contributing
a major portion of the selectivity of the receiver.

All right now—have you found the adjustments on the i-f transformers?
Tune in a local broadcast station and shorten the receiver antenna so that
the station provides a mid-scale deflection on the S-meter of your set. Pick
out one of the i-f transformer trimmers at random, and make a mental note
of the position. Pencil a mark on the transformer case indicating the setting
of the trimmer, if you wish. Now, take your insulated alignment tool and
slowly turn the trimmer one way and then the other. Watch the S-meter
while you do this. You will note that the adjustment is not critical, and
the signal will get a little weaker, or a little stronger as you move the
trimmer. Adjust the trimmer for maximum reading of the S-meter. Check
and see if the trimmer is in the same position as when you started the test.
If not, this adjustment was out of alignment, and you've corrected the error.

Fig. 3 Chassis layout of tube-type receiver. Slugs for oscillator coils are adjacent
to the main tuning capacitor, with bandspread capacitor at right. I-f transformers
and tubes are in foreground, with power transformer at left.

I-F Amplifier Alignment

Now that you have the "hang" of it, you can align the whole i-f amplifier. Start with the *last* i-f transformer (the one between the last i-f tube and the second detector) and progress forward towards the mixer transformer. If your receiver has a crystal filter, you had better leave the adjustments on it alone for the time being, as it is a foxy business to properly align the filter. It is necessary, however, to make sure that the i-f amplifier of your receiver is properly aligned to the crystal frequency of the filter. Be sure you tune your receiver so that the test signal is properly centered in the pass-band of the crystal. To accomplish this, switch on the filter and tune the receiver for highest S-meter reading of the test signal. Take it easy! The crystal peak is very sharp. When you are "on the nose," you can align your i-f transformers for maximum reading of the meter. Check the receiver tuning. If the receiver drifts a bit, you might have to repeak the signal to prevent it from drifting off the peak of the crystal. With practice, you can actually align the i-f stages by ear, and you'll probably have to do this if your receiver has no S-meter.

As an example, a top view of the chassis of a medium-priced receiver is illustrated in Figure 3. I-f transformers are in the foreground. The iron core trimmers can be easily adjusted through holes in the top and bottom

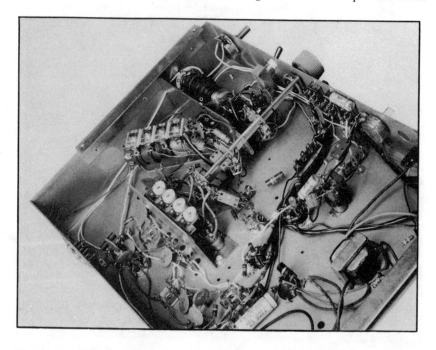

Fig. 4 Under-chassis components of tube-type receiver. R-f coils and alignment capacitors are grouped closely around the bandswitch. Oscillator coils are behind the bandswitch, with r-f coils at upper left and mixer coils directly below. Transistor-style receiver would have same approximate layout.

of the transformers. The bottom slug holes can be seen in figure 4. Start the alignment from the "rear end" of the i-f amplifier. Align the slugs of the last, middle and first transformers. Tune for highest S-meter reading of a moderately strong signal. It makes no difference which transformer slug you adjust first, and you can change the order of alignment if you wish, but the "tail-end-first" method is generally used for a score of obscure reasons.

While you are at it, you might as well align the beat frequency oscillator (b-f-o). In most receivers, a triode tube is used as the b-f-o for c-w and single sideband reception. The purpose is to provide a heterodyne against the incoming signal so that code or SSB transmission can be made intelligible. The b-f-o is actually a miniature signal generator, tuned to the intermediate frequency and coupled to the i-f amplifier. If the b-f-o is tuned to 456 kc it will produce a one kc audible beat with an i-f signal on 455 kc. Because the a-v-c circuit of the receiver will rectify the signal of the beat oscillator, producing a strong a-v-c voltage and a consequent drop in receiver gain whenever the b-f-o and a-v-c are both functioning, the a-v-c is normally disconnected whenever the b-f-o is used. For purposes of b-f-o alignment, however, the a-v-c may be left on, if desired. The antenna is removed from the receiver and the b-f-o tuning control *(pitch* control) on the panel is set at the center position. This permits the control to rotate an equal number of degrees to the right and to the left. With the knob in the center, the b-f-o should be tuned to the intermediate frequency of the receiver. Find the adjustment control on the beat oscillator transformer. In most cases it is a slug adjustment mounted atop the unit. Turn on the b-f-o and adjust the slug one way or the other. Slowly tune it and note the hiss heard in the speaker. Tune the trimmer of the b-f-o transformer back and forth, and adjust it so the hiss has the lowest pitch. Turning the trimmer in either direction from the correct setting should raise the pitch of the hiss. If the trimmer is turned far enough in either direction, this hiss will rise in pitch and gradually get weaker. Bring it back into audibility and adjust the trimmer as described. The beat oscillator is now tuned to the center of the i-f passband. It may be detuned slightly to one side or the other of the passband by varying the vernier panel control. In most instances, this pitch control is a variable capacitor, but in some solid state receivers it is a potentiometer.

Your i-f stages are now properly aligned. It is well to check the alignment every year or so to make sure that the adjustments do not drift out of alignment. In most cases the stages will "stay put," but it is wise to make sure. Also check alignment whenever the i-f tubes are changed. *Summary: The i-f circuits of your receiver are aligned by trimmer adjustments mounted within the i-f transformers. These trimmers control the gain and the selectivity of your receiver. Adjust the trimmers for maximum strength of a steady, local signal. Peak each trimmer for maximum S-meter reading of the signal.*

R-F ALIGNMENT OF YOUR RECEIVER

The main drawback of the superhetrodyne receiver is that it is capable of simultaneous reception on two different frequencies at the same time.

The unwanted frequency is called the *image frequency*. Reception of the image signal may be substantially eliminated by the use of a radio frequency amplifier stage placed ahead of the converter stage of the receiver. The image frequency is displaced from the wanted frequency by twice the amount of the intermediate frequency. Thus, if we were listening to a station on 14,000 kc with a receiver having a 455 kc i-f stage, a signal on the image frequency of 14,910 could be heard in the receiver. A good r-f stage can amplify the 14,000 kc signal and reject the image signal. Many of the inexpensive short wave receivers on the market have no r-f stage for reasons of economy, and these receivers are bothered by unwanted image signals. The r-f amplifier stage also increases the overall sensitivity of the receiver to a great degree. No shortwave receiver can be called a true communications receiver unless it has a good r-f amplifier stage ahead of the first converter tube, similar to that shown in Figure 5 .

R-f alignment, therefore, is extremely important since maximum sensitivity and optimum image rejection both depend upon accurate tuning of the r-f and mixer circuits of the receiver. Look at the bottom view of the typical receiver shown in Figure 4. The r-f stage coils are located in the far corner of the receiver. The antenna and grid coils for the three lowest frequency bands (L1A, L1B, L1C) are wound on one form, and the r-f coil for the highest frequency band (L2, 14-40 mc) is wound on a separate form, mounted next to the bandswitch deck, S1A. The schematic of this section of the receiver is shown in Figure 6. This receiver has an auxiliary antenna trimmer (C1) mounted atop the chassis, adjacent to the 6BA6 r-f amplifier tube. All that is required to bring the circuit into alignment is to tune the trimmer for maximum strength of the incoming signal. Easy, isn't it? There are no other adjustments that need to be made to this group of r-f coils.

Other receiver designs, however, may employ separate r-f trimmers connected across each coil. This is done in the more expensive receivers (Figure 7). Each high frequency r-f coil has its own trimmer capacitor, in addition to having an adjustable slug for the high frequency coils. No panel antenna trimmer control is required. The individual bands are adjusted for maximum sensitivity by changing the inductance of the coil (L1, L2) at the *low frequency* end of the tuning range, and adjusting the trimmer capacitor (C1, C2) at the *high frequency* end of the tuning range. The trimmers that accomplish this are shown in the under-chassis drawing of Figure 8.

Assume the "number three' band (4.5—13.0 mc) is to be aligned. The

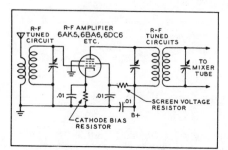

Fig. 5 Simple radio frequency amplifier placed ahead of mixer tube reduces tendency of superheterodyne circuit to receive two frequencies at once. R-f amplifier reduces the response to unwanted signals.

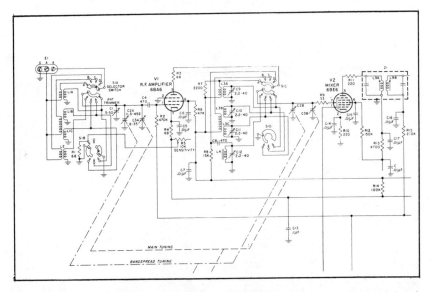

Fig. 6 R-f circuit of tube-type receiver, showing bandchange switch and band-spread tuning arrangement. R-f amplifier stage provides good signal-to-noise ratio and good a-v-c response. Transistorized stages are similar.

receiver is first tuned to a steady signal near 5.0 mc. This signal might be an r-f generator attached to the antenna terminals of the receiver, or it might be a loud station operating near that frequency. The slug of antenna coil L2 is tuned for maximum signal as read on the S-meter of the receiver. When the slug has been adjusted properly, the receiver is tuned to 12 mc, and the capacitor trimmer (C2) is adjusted for best signal response at this frequency. These adjustments mutually affect each other, and tend to be slightly interlocking. If much change in the trimmer setting is made at one end of the band, the other adjustment probably should be retouched for maximum response.

The same procedure is followed for the mixer stage of the receiver. If the mixer coils have tuning slugs, they should be adjusted for maximum signal response at the low frequency end of the tuning dial. The trimmer capacitors are adjusted for maximum response at the high frequency end of the dial. You should adjust the coil slugs first, then follow up by adjusting the trimmer capacitors.

The mixer circuit trimmer capacitors of a typical receiver may be seen in Figure 4 (C9, C10, C11, C12) and in the circuit of Figure 6. The mixer coils for the three low frequency bands are adjusted at the factory and do not require slug manipulation. The mixer coil for the high frequency (D) band is slug tuned by a small powdered iron core threaded inside of the form. Adjustment of the slug is made near the low frequency end of the dial.

In most cases—especially if the receiver is new and does not exhibit any "dead spots" in the tuning range—the adjustment slugs can be left alone, and all minor alignments can be made at the high frequency end of each

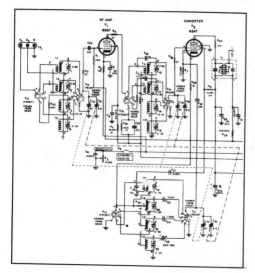

Fig. 7   R-f amplifier and mixer of inexpensive tube-type set. Either metal or glass tubes may be used in this representative circuit. R-f circuits are at the left, with mixer coils at center. Oscillator coils are at bottom of the diagram. Transistor stages are similar in design.

dial range by peaking the trimmer capacitors. If you have no signal generator, this can be done by listening to the background noise level of the receiver. Adjust the trimmer for maximum background noise at the high frequency end of each band. If the background noise drops off toward the low frequency end of the tuning dial, it indicates the coil adjustment must be varied a bit to "pep" up reception at that end of the dial.

The mixer circuit of a tube-type receiver is shown in Fig. 7. The two high frequency coils (L4, L5) are slug-tuned for low frequency adjustment, and have trimmer capacitors (C12, C13) for high frequency alignment. The two low frequency coils are adjusted at the factory for proper inductance, and have capacitor trimmers (C14, C15) for alignment at the high frequency ends of the respective bands. Compare the circuits of Figure 6 and Figure 7 with the "front end" circuit of your receiver, and you can easily spot the adjustment points in your set. You can approach these adjustments with impunity, as none of them will affect the dial calibration of the receiver. The r-f and mixer circuits can actually be peaked by ear, or with the aid of the S-meter and a few steady signals. The time spent in checking the alignment of these circuits will pay big dividends in better reception.

Recently the author bought a new all-wave receiver in the $300 price class. It performed well, but seemed to be a little "flat" on the 10 and 15 meter amateur bands. Signals could be heard, to be sure, but the set didn't exhibit the "sock" that should have been apparent. After a little examination, it was noticed that the 10 meter image signals were almost as loud as the fundamental signals. Peaking the r-f trimmer control on the panel of the receiver made little difference in the degree of image rejection or receiver sensitivity. Acting on the hunch that the mixer stage circuit might be misaligned, the receiver was removed from the cabinet and turned on end. A quick perusal of the instruction book soon located the trimmer capacitors of the mixer stage. The receiver was tuned to the high frequency end of the dial (31 mc) and the mixer trimmer was carefully adjusted for maximum background noise. The receiver awoke with a bang, as the background level picked up with just a small tweak of the trimmer. Ten meter signals appeared as if from nowhere when the receiver was tuned across the ham band. The image signals were suitably attenuated. When the r-f trimmer on the panel of the set was tuned through resonance the peak in background noise could clearly be noticed. Within five minutes of the time the receiver was taken from the cabinet, the adjustment was made, and the receiver was returned to the cabinet in good working order.

Summary: The r-f and mixer tuned circuits of the receiver determine the sensitivity and image rejection of the receiver. To insure proper tracking of the circuits across a whole band, the inductance of the r-f and mixer coils in use must be adjusted for maximum signal response at the low frequency end of the tuning range. The trimmer capacitor for each stage must then be adjusted for maximum signal response at the high frequency end of each range. Since the inductance of the coils is not subject to drastic changes as is the capacitance of the trimmers, it may often suffice to peak the circuit padders for optimum reception near the high frequency end of each tuning range.

THE HIGH FREQUENCY OSCILLATOR

The *converter stage* of the receiver (often called a *first detector* or *mixer)* changes the frequency of the incoming signal to the frequency of the fixed-tuned intermediate frequency amplifier. A special multi-grid converter tube may be used, one portion acting as the mixing unit, and the second portion serving as the high frequency (conversion) oscillator. These functions may also be accomplished by two separate tubes. The small r-f signal generated by the oscillator is combined with the incoming signal within the mixing tube, and the resulting "beat" signal is generated at the intermediate frequency, ready to fall into the waiting arms of the i-f amplifier.

As the dial of the superheterodyne receiver is tuned, the high frequency oscillator follows the frequency of reception, but always at a fixed distance away from it in frequency. This frequency difference is arithmetically equal to the intermediate frequency, as discussed in chapter 4. Since the mixer can act upon all signals that are removed from the desired frequency by the amount of the intermediate frequency, it is the job of the r-f stage to pick out the desired signal and to reject the undesired (image) signal. So far, so good. The main goal in life of the high frequency oscillator, therefore, is to tag along a respectful distance away from the r-f circuits and to supply the necessary beating signal at this frequency.

Yes, it is a genuine radio signal, too! The high frequency oscillator of any receiver is actually a pee-wee radio transmitter, generating a flea-power signal that may be heard some distance away from the receiver. During the last war this interesting fact was put to good use by the U.S. Navy. They would search for and find the frequency the enemy used to send messages to his naval ships. Since the ships maintained radio silence, and only used their receivers, the enemy felt sure that the ships could not be detected. The Navy found the frequency of transmission to the ships, and then tuned sensitive direction finders to the frequency of the conversion oscillator in

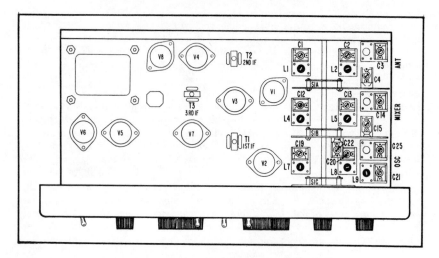

Fig. 8 Under-chassis layout of inexpensive, tube-type receiver, showing placement of parts. Solid state receiver layout is similar to this.

the enemy receiver. They knew the oscillator was either 455 kc higher or lower in frequency than the channel the message was being sent on. Two such direction finders would give the bearing and range of the receiver for an accurate "fix." A salvo of gun fire would quickly spell the end of the enemy ship. This system worked both ways, and soon all concerned learned how to suppress oscillator radiation in their receivers to prevent detection by the enemy. Your receiver does not require such suppression, and you can hear the high frequency oscillator of your set in a nearby receiver. Tune the auxiliary receiver 455 kc higher or lower in frequency than the dial reading of your set, and you will probably hear the oscillator S-9 plus.

Frequency Calibration of Your Receiver

The dial of your receiver is probably calibrated in terms of frequency. Do not jump to the conclusion that your receiver is as accurate as WWV! It isn't, and it isn't meant to be! Frequency meters designed to check frequencies in the shortwave range cost over a thousand dollars—and are built like a battleship, not like a receiver. Once again, the receiver manufacturer must make a compromise between calibration accuracy and receiver cost. Too many embryo amateurs believe that the dial calibration of their receiver is the Gospel Truth, and adjust their transmitter frequency accordingly. That is why the Federal Communications Commission monitoring stations are working overtime to log the many offenders that trespass outside the legal limits of the amateur bands! The dial calibration of your receiver is a close generalization that will match the majority of a production run of perhaps five hundred or a thousand receivers. If your receiver calibration is "on the nose" across all the bands, you deserve the gold medal with two peanut clusters. When you take the time to examine your receiver calibration closely with the aid of a *good* frequency standard, you will find that the calibration error is not bad—not bad at all, and probably inversely

"As I understand it, the poor chap couldn't decide on which side of the signal to place the local oscillator!"

proportional to the amount of money that you paid for the receiver!

Calibration Errors

If the high frequency oscillator is not detuned from the reception frequency by the proper amount, a simple frequency error will result. If the oscillator is supposed to jog along 455 kc higher in frequency than the received signal, and through some maladjustment it remains only 430 kc away, the dial calibration error will be the error-difference in frequency, or 25 kilocycles. This error will remain constant across the dial, that is, the calibration error will be the same at both ends of the dial.

The smart reader who has digested chapter 4 will remember that the high frequency oscillator tunes at a different *percentage* tuning rate than that of the r-f and mixer circuits. While the oscillator covers the same *number* of kilocycles covered by the r-f circuits, the percentage change from one end of the tuning range to the other as compared to the r-f and mixer circuits is *not* the same. This interesting fact means that the calibration error at one end of the tuning dial can be different from the error at the other end of the dial. It is the frequency of the conversion oscillator that determines the exact frequency of reception, regardless of what markings the tuning dial may happen to have! For example, the dial calibration error might be 25 kilocycles low at the high frequency end of a particular band. At this spot the h-f-o is 25 kilocycles away from where it should be. At the low frequency end of the same band, the dial calibration error might be 375 kilocycles high. The oscillator has strayed 375 kilocycles from the correct frequency. The calibration error can either be high or low at either end of the band, and it can be different at each end! This type of misalignment is called *tracking error*.

The upshot of this whole business is that dial calibration accuracy is almost proportional to the cost of the receiver, and to the care the manufacturer takes in aligning the oscillator circuits. Just because your receiver cost a lot of money do not assume the dial calibrations are correct. They may be no more correct than the calibration of a second-hand "cracker box." *But* the expensive receiver has adjustment points that permit the tracking to be aligned very closely to the dial calibrations with the expenditure of a little of your time. The calibration of the "cracker box" will always be in error, since there is no means of making compensating adjustments. The low cost of the set precluded inclusion of expensive trimmers and adjustment slugs. The luxury of accurate dial calibration costs money, and you must pay for it!

The chief engineer of a large receiver manufacturer once told the author that it cost over twenty dollars of labor time to correctly align one of the company's expensive receivers. This was almost equal to the profit they hoped to make on the receiver! In order to reduce the alignment cost the receivers were adjusted at only *one spot* on each band, near the middle of the dial. The engineer admitted that the alignment job was mediocre and that dial calibration was left pretty much to chance. "It was the only thing we could do," he explained. "Anyway, the receiver was a good one, and the owner who knew the ropes could always adjust the receiver for perfect alignment. We simply could not afford to spend the extra money necessary to provide a first-class alignment job." The receiver in question was a fine one and had plenty of reserve gain. The owner who did not worry about dial calibration probably never noted the "quick-and-dirty" alignment technique used on the receiver. Everyone was happy except the chief engineer. He developed ulcers shortly after the new aligning technique went into use.

HIGH OR LOW?

It can be seen that the conversion oscillator of a receiver can be placed either on the low frequency side or the high frequency side of the tuned circuits of the mixer and r-f stage. In the great majority of cases, the high frequency position is chosen. That is, the oscillator is always 455 kilocycles *higher in frequency* than that of the received signal. In a few receivers (such as the *Hammarlund HQ-140* series) the oscillator is placed on the low frequency side of the incoming signal. You can be sure that "high side" operation is employed if series trimmer capacitors are used in the oscillator circuit (C28, C29, C30 of Figure 11, and C23, C24, and C25 of Figure 7). Usually no oscillator series trimmer capacitor is required for the highest frequency band, and the oscillator may be placed on either side of the incoming signal. Many receivers place the oscillator on the "low side" on this band. Unfortunately, this point is seldom mentioned in the instruction manual. Be sure you know on which side of the signal the high frequency oscillator of your receiver operates before you start to play with the alignment trimmers! If you inadvertently "flop sides" and get the oscillator on the wrong side of the signal, you can tweak the trimmers all day and you will never be able to make the oscillator tracking match the dial calibration! Too few instruction books provide this necessary information, which can often only be obtained by writing to the manufacturer of the receiver.

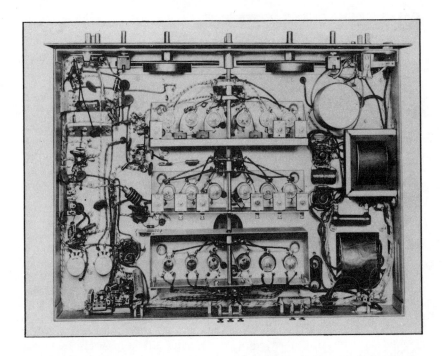

Fig. 9   Under-chassis view of Hammarlund HQ-140XA. High frequency coils are arranged in three banks around bandchange switch at center of receiver. The power supply is at right, with i-f amplifier and tubes along left of the chassis.

OSCILLATOR ADJUSTMENT

If you know a few of the landmarks, you can thread your way through the wilderness of receiver alignment with comparative ease. The first landmark is the frequency of the i-f amplifier. This will tell you the displacement of the high frequency oscillator from the signal. Unless warning landmarks indicate to the contrary, you can assume the oscillator is placed on the high frequency side of the signal. Thus if you have a receiver that is far out of alignment, and you know the receiver has an i-f of 455 kc you can easily whip the set into quick alignment. Tune the receiver dial to 15 mc and put an antenna on the receiver. Adjust the oscillator trimmer until you hear WWV. The oscillator is now on 15,455 kc. You can now proceed with a polished alignment job, once you have established yourself with a familiar landmark.

The high frequency oscillator determines the accuracy of dial calibration of your receiver. The tuning range of the oscillator may be adjusted in the same manner as the tuning range of the receiver r-f circuits. That is, oscillator calibration is adjusted first to the low frequency end of each range by varying the inductance of the oscillator coil. The receiver is next tuned

Fig. 10 High speed tape recorders in the Washington, D. C. studios of VOA provide almost instantaneous copy of interviews with visiting dignitaries, special events of worldwide interest, and musical programs. More than 50,000 recordings are made every year, for translation and broadcast in many languages.

to the high frequency end of the dial, and oscillator calibration is adjusted at this point by means of the oscillator trimmer capacitor. The oscillator tuning slugs of a typical medium-priced set are seen in Figure 3, and the high frequency calibration trimmers are visible in Figure 4. Notice that low-drift ceramic capacitors are employed in the oscillator circuit to insure frequency stability with respect to ambient temperature.

The coil catacomb of the *Hammarlund HQ-140XA* receiver is shown in Figure 9. Notice that ceramic capacitors are used on the high frequency oscillator coils for maximum frequency stability, and that all of the mixer and oscillator coils are slug-tuned for tracking purposes. As with many receivers, slug tuning of the oscillator coils is used to achieve "low-end" alignment of the r-f circuits.

The circuit of a typical high frequency oscillator is shown in Figure 11. You will notice in the top view of this receiver (Figure 3) that the plates of the oscillator section of the tuning capacitor are not cut to a special shape as are those of the inexpensive ac-dc broadcast set. Such an expedient will work over the broadcast band, but is definitely unsuited for shortwave operation. In order to maintain the desired *percentage* frequency difference between the oscillator and the r-f circuits, a series padding capacitor is added to the oscillator circuit (C28, C29, and C30 of Figure 11). The value of each series capacitor is carefully chosen at the factory to maintain the correct percentage frequency difference as the circuits of the receiver are tuned. Since the percentage rate is the same across a given band, the series padder capacitor may be a fixed unit.

You will notice that this capacitor increases in value for each successively higher frequency band, and the highest frequency band requires no capacitor at all. This is because the percentage frequency difference becomes a smaller factor as the frequency reception is increased, and the reactance of the capacitor may be reduced accordingly. On the highest band, the required capacitive reactance is so small that the capacitor may be omitted with no

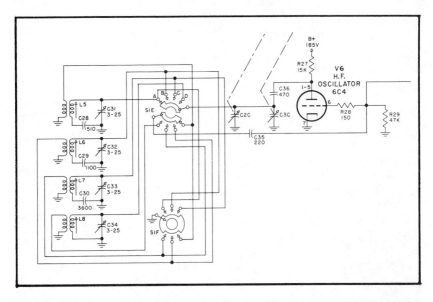

Fig. 11 Oscillator circuit of tube-type receiver. Transistorized circuit is similar. Stability is mainly a function of mechanical assembly and the precision of component parts. Supply voltage is often stabilized.

detrimental effect upon receiver performance. Many medium-priced receivers employ a variable series capacitor (C25, Figure 7) for broadcast band tracking. This adjustment is made at the low frequency end of the band (near 600 kc) for correct dial calibration and minimum tracking error.

Complete oscillator alignment should follow the procedure outlined later in this chapter. If the calibration error is not great, slight adjustments may be made to the trimmer and the oscillator coil slug to bring the receiver into calibration. Stations whose frequencies are accurately known may be used as "markers" (WWV, for example), or a crystal calibrator such as the one described in chapter 6 of this Handbook may be used. Low frequency dial calibration is done with the slug of the oscillator coil, and high frequency adjustment is done with the trimmer capacitor. These adjustments tend to be interlocking, and calibration at both ends of the dial should be checked after any adjustment is made. Keep a record of the dial error, and you can soon see if your efforts are making an improvement in calibration.

COMPLETE RECEIVER ALIGNMENT PROCEDURE

If the necessary equipment is at hand, a complete alignment job may be done on your receiver with little trouble. It is an interesting task, and you will learn a lot about receiver operation if you undertake to do this. You will need three pieces of equipment: A signal generator, an output meter, and an alignment tool. A block diagram of the test set-up is shown in Figure 12, and a photo of an actual alignment run on a *Hammarlund*

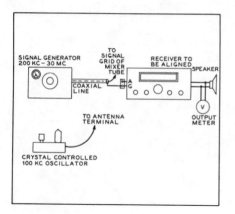

Fig. 12 Tuneable signal generator is used for rough alignment of the receiver. Tracking and frequency check requires accurately known sets of frequencies, most easily obtained from crystal calibrator.

receiver is illustrated in Figure 13. A vacuum-tube voltmeter (or other high impedance voltmeter) is used, along with an accurate signal generator. Kit-type instruments are excellent for this purpose.

Preliminary Inspection

Examine all soldered joints. Look for frayed wires, loose screws and nuts. Clean the dust from the components. Apply power to the set, and observe that all tube heaters glow. Look for signs of short circuits and smoke. Measure all the important d-c voltages with the vacuum tube volt-meter and compare these readings with the values given in the receiver instruction book.

Intermediate-Frequency Alignment

Attach the vacuum tube voltmeter (v-t-v-m) to the speaker output terminals, and set it on a low a-c range (5 volts). Connect the output of the signal generator to the input circuit of the mixer stage through a .01 uf paper capacitor. Ground the shield of the generator coaxial line to the chassis of the receiver. (Note: If the receiver is an ac-dc set, ground the shield of the generator line through a .01 uf paper capacitor to the chassis of the receiver.)

With the signal generator tuned to 455 kc and modulated 30% at 400 cycles, increase the output of the generator to provide an indication on the v-t-v-m output meter. Reduce the range of the meter to 1.5 volts and adjust the output level of the signal generator for half-scale reading of the v-t-v-m. (Note: Check your receiver instruction book for the proper audio signal level at the v-t-v-m. It varies from receiver to receiver.) Tune the trimmers of each i-f transformer (starting with the last) for maximum indication on the output meter. Reduce the r-f output of the signal generator as needed to prevent receiver overload. Recheck alignment of the transformers until you are sure they are carefully peaked. If a crystal filter is incorporated in the receiver, check your instruction manual for alignment information.

Remove the tone modulation from the signal generator, and switch the receiver to c-w operation. Connect headphones to the receiver. Adjust the

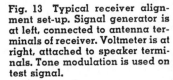

Fig. 13 Typical receiver alignment set-up. Signal generator is at left, connected to antenna terminals of receiver. Voltmeter is at right, attached to speaker terminals. Tone modulation is used on test signal.

b-f-o trimmer to produce a zero-beat in the phones with the panel pitch control of the b-f-o in center position. Turn pitch control through its range. The beat note should vary smoothly as the control is varied above and below zero beat.

Oscillator Alignment

A crystal controlled marker generator is convenient for oscillator alignment, although a well calibrated signal generator may be used for r-f and mixer adjustments. Some receivers have 100 kc marker generators built-in that can be used for the following tests.

Couple the output of the marker generator to the antenna terminals of the receiver. Check each band of the receiver to see that the marker signals can be heard at 100 kilocycle intervals across the dial. The procedure is to align the oscillator circuits to the correct frequency at the low end of each band by adjusting coil inductance for maximum signal output. The high frequency end of the ranges are then set to frequency by adjusting the trimmer capacitors. These operations are then repeated until both ends of the range are tuned to the correct dial calibration points.

Broadcast band. Tune receiver until the 600 kc marker signal shows an indication on the S-meter. Adjust the oscillator coil slug until the signal peaks at the correct dial frequency. Keep the signal level low to avoid overloading the receiver. Tune receiver until the 1500 kc marker signal is heard. Adjust the trimmer capacitor of the oscillator to peak the signal at the correct dial frequency. Recheck low end calibration and realign coil slug if necessary. Any change in inductance will require a change in trimmer capacitance. Recheck until both ends of range are on the proper settings, always setting the high frequency end of the band last. If a variable oscillator series capacitor is used, it may be adjusted slightly to change the tuning *rate* of the oscillator. This will vary the tuning "distance" between the end points of the band. Always treat the series padding capacitor as a "last resort" adjustment, and try and obtain alignment without touching it.

Shortwave bands. Adjustment of these bands follows the procedure outlined above. Care must be taken to use the correct marker signal, as many of them will be heard as the receiver is tuned across the band. It is a good idea to spot the correct marker signal by zero-beating it with the signal generator. A marker signal of known frequency is chosen near the low frequency end of each band. The *inductance* (slug) of the proper oscillator coil is slowly adjusted in small steps, until the marker signal is heard at the correct point on the dial. It is common practice to choose calibration points about one megacycle in from the ends of the dial to simplify the alignment problem. On the higher frequency bands, trouble may be had differentiating between the marker signal and its image, especially if the oscillator circuits are misaligned. The variable frequency signal generator should be zero-beat with a convenient marker signal and used for preliminary alignment. If the local oscillator of the receiver should be on the *high frequency* side of the signal, the following adjustment must be made: Turn the oscillator slug all the way out. As the slug is turned in, two points will be noticed at which the signal generator may be heard. The *first* signal (slug furthest out) is the correct tuning point. This is true only if the oscillator frequency *decreases* as the slug is inserted within the coil. This tuning sequence may be checked by tuning in the image signal, which should appear at a dial reading approximately 910 kilocycles *below* that of the real signal. If the oscillator operates on the *low frequency* side of the signal, the *second* tuning peak (slug furthest in) should be used.

The high frequency dial calibration should now be set. The signal generator is now zero-beat with a marker of known frequency near the high frequency end of the tuning dial. Standard frequency station WWV can often be used to identify the frequency setting of the signal generator, or to provide a known calibration point for the receiver. The oscillator trimmer capacitor is adjusted to receive the signal at the correct point on the dial. On the high frequency band, it is possible to find two points on the capacitor adjustment at which the signal generator may be heard. One point is the correct one, and the other one is the image point. If the local oscillator of the receiver operates on the "high side" of the signal, use the setting which provides the smallest value of capacitance. This adjustment may be checked by tuning in the image signal, which should appear at a dial reading approximately 910 kilocycles *below* that of the real signal. Conversely, if "low side" operation is desired, use the setting providing the highest value of capacitance. The image signal will now be 910 kilocycles *above* the real signal.

Once the preliminary adjustments have been made, the crystal calibrator marker signals may be used to make final corrections to the dial calibration. Recheck the low frequency calibration point, and reset it if necessary. Any change in the position of the coil slug will require a readjustment of the trimmer capacitor at the high frequency calibration point as these adjustments tend to be interlocking. Recheck until both ends of the range are on the proper dial settings, always setting the high frequency calibration point last. It should be possible to maintain a calibration accuracy of greater than 0.5% at these points. That is, the calibration error should be less than 150 kilocycles on the main tuning dial at 30,000 kc. With care you can reduce it below this figure.

Be sure and let the receiver run for an hour or two before you align the oscillator. Check the frequency drift caused by thermal heating of the

"Here's yer shortwave set, Buddy!"

chassis and components. It may be necessary to retouch the adjustments to bring the calibration back into line. In any case, it is smart to do the oscillator alignment job after the receiver has reached operating temperature.

R-F and Mixer Stage Alignment

The next job is to adjust the mixer and r-f tuned circuits so that they track properly with the oscillator. These circuits are tuned to the frequency indicated on the receiver dial, whereas the oscillator circuit has been adjusted 455 kilocycles higher or lower in frequency than the dial calibration. The variable signal generator may be used as a signal source, since frequency accuracy is not required.

Alignment procedure is the same for all bands. The signal generator is tuned to the low frequency end of the band, and is adjusted to provide a half-scale reading on the S-meter of the receiver. The inductance of the r-f coil and the mixer coil is varied by means of the coil slug for maximum signal indication on the meter. The signal generator is then tuned to a spot near the high frequency end of the band, and the r-f and mixer trimmer capacitors are adjusted for maximum signal strength. Retune the receiver to the low frequency end of the dial, and note the position of the r-f and mixer trimmers. Repeak the trimmers for maximum received signal at this frequency and note the new setting for both. If the mixer and r-f trimmers do not peak at the same setting in the above two tests, vary the inductance of the coils slightly and repeat the test. It should be possible to have both r-f and mixer trimmers peak at approximately the same setting for both ends of the band. Be sure that you do this test on the actual signal, and not upon the image signal. It can be noticed that the r-f and mixer trimmers will produce two peaks in the background noise on the higher frequency bands. One peak is the correct one, the other is the image peak. On the latter, the tuned circuits are peaked on the incorrect side of the high frequency oscillator. If the oscillator operates on the high frequency side of the incoming signal, the correct noise peak is the one that occurs at the greater capacity setting of the trimmers. Conversely, if the oscillator operates on the low frequency side of the incoming signal, the trimmers should be aligned on the noise peak that occurs at the lesser capacity. When alignment is completed, the image signal will appear 910 kc *below* the real signal if the oscillator is operating on the high frequency side of the incoming signal, and 910 kc *above* the real signal if the oscillator is operating on the low frequency side of the incoming signal.

Errors in Tracking

After the high frequency oscillator, r-f amplifier, and mixer circuits have been aligned, tracking at any point in the spectrum may be checked by adjusting the signal generator to the proper frequency and testing the settings of the r-f and mixer trimmers for maximum gain. Frequency calibration may also be checked at these points. After such a test, all trimmers should be reset at the high frequency end of the band since their settings are most critical at this point.

Tracking errors at the low frequency end of the band can be caused by errors in the tuning capacitor sections, the value of the coil inductance, or the high frequency oscillator series capacitance. In order to determine if one or more sections of the master tuning capacitor are the cause of mistracking, it is necessary to make the check described above on two or more different bands. If the same tracking error appears on all bands, the master tuning capacitor is at fault. The error may be corrected by permanently bending the slotted rotor plates of the capacitor to provide the proper amount of correction.

If the tracking error appears only in the r-f amplifier or mixer stage, and only on one band, the inductance of the coil of the particular stage is at fault or the series padding capacitor is an incorrect value. Some oscillator coils have a moveable turn or loop that may be varied slightly to correct the inductance. Others may be corrected by movement of the variable slug mounted within the coil.

The series padding capacitor for the oscillator (in the great majority of receivers) is a hand-picked low-drift mica or ceramic unit that is not adjustable. If it seems certain that this capacitor is in error, it should be carefully removed from the circuit and measured on a capacity bridge. Replacement units may be obtained from the receiver manufacturer or his accredited service organization.

How Good Is My Receiver?

This argument rages at all radio club meetings, among the amateurs on the air, and at the counters of the radio stores. In fact, it is one of the general topics of conversation whenever two radio enthusiasts get together. Each receiver manufacturer has his own enthusiastic group of exuberant

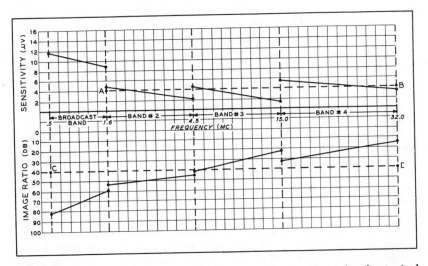

Fig. 14 Sensitivity and Signal-to-Image Ratio is shown above for the typical all-wave receiver of the $150 price range. Sensitivity is adequate over the entire range, but S/I ratio is poor above 5 mc. Image signals are troublesome, particularly on the 20, 15, and 10 meter amateur bands. An extra r-f stage (preselector) will do much to reduce the image signals and improve the signal to noise ratio and sensitivity above 14 mc. The image problem also may be substantially eliminated by the double conversion receiver. The low sensitivity is an asset on broadcast band, as it helps to reduce overload from strong stations.

boosters, and a small tightly-knit clique of knockers. The cherished receiver of one ham is the pet gripe of his best friend. "Never buy a *Floppola-8!* They are a pile of junk. You can't hear *anything* with one of those lemons," says one ham. *The Floppola-8?* Best receiver I ever had," says another. "Used it for my weekly sked with Inner Slobbovia for two years and never missed a word!"

The truth usually lies somewhere between these two violent extremes. When you remember that the original signal plucked out of the air is of the order of a few microvolts, *receiving anything at all* seems like a large order. In general, the old axiom, "you get what you pay for" certainly applies to receivers. Your pocketbook is generally a good guide to receiver performance.

Radio manufacturers are somewhat loath to release specific information about their products, and rightly so. Detailed information would not mean much to the average buyer, and it is a function of the type and technique of measurement. Thus information produced by one manufacturer would not necessarily be based upon the same measurements and operating conditions used by another. Comparison of the two groups of information, therefore, would be meaningless. Then too, many manufacturers shy clear of talking too much about the specific performance of their products in order to protect themselves against other less scrupulous manufacturers who dream up their performance characteristics in the advertising department, rather than in the engineering office.

Typical Receiver Performance

With little trouble it is easy to reach a broad plateau of agreement concerning receiver specifications. These "specs" are deliberately vague, but they can provide a yardstick by which a receiver may be judged. The two basic points of interest to all receiver owners are *receiver sensitivity* and *signal to image ratio* (S/I). These points do not define all the excellent characteristics or all the faults of a receiver. A certain set can excel in these features, yet have drift, hum, and poor overload performance in the presence of a strong signal. However, this is a good place to start, so let's look at a typical receiver in the $150 price range and see just how it measures up to these requirements.

An arbitrary performance specification might state that satisfactory receiver performance can be defined as entailing a minimum sensitivity level of 4 microvolts and a signal-to-image ratio of 40 decibels. The sensitivity specification refers to the minimum value of input signal required to produce an audio signal that is 10 decibels above the noise of the receiver. Taking these specifications at their face value, we can apply them to the mythical receiver under examination. This receiver is a nine tube set, having one r-f stage and a 455 kc i-f amplifier. It covers 550 kc to 32.0 mc in four tuning ranges. The sensitivity and S/I ratio curves are shown in Figure 14. Sensitivity is deliberately reduced on the broadcast band to about 10 microvolts to eliminate cross-talk and overloading that might be caused by strong local stations. Extreme sensitivity is not required for this band as local atmospheric noise will mask the receiver sensitivity in any case. Image rejection is best at the low frequency end of the band, being over 80 db. The image ratio drops to about 60 db at the high frequency end of the broadcast band. This deterioration in S/I ratio is normal, and is a function of the ratio of inductance to capacitance in the tuned circuits at any given frequency. You can see from Figure 14 that the best S/I ratio occurs when the receiver is tuned to the low frequency end of each band.

The sensitivity in each shortwave band is acceptable, being better than 6 microvolts on each band. This is sufficient to allow the listener to hear the "background noise" picked up by the antenna at all frequencies except perhaps those above 25 mc or so. The external noise level on the 10 meter (28—29.7 mc) amateur band is quite low and signals having strengths of the order of 0.5—5.0 microvolts can be heard. This particular set will probably miss these "real weak ones." Notice that the sensitivity of the receiver is at maximum at the high frequency end of each tuning range. This is because the most favorable coupling conditions between the r-f coils of the receiver occur at minimum capacity setting, and is one reason why the manufacturers like to place each amateur band so that it falls at the top end of each tuning range. This insures that the receiver will be "hot" in the ham bands.

If we hold to our concept of a signal-to-image ratio of 40 db as being satisfactory performance, we see that this particular set falls below that requirement above 5 megacycles. This means that image signals of strong 40 meter amateurs can be found on the receiver by looking for them, that images of 20 meter signals will be apparent, and that images of 15 meter amateurs will be very noticeable. Images of 10 meter amateurs will be almost as loud as the fundamental signal, being reduced in strength by only about 15 db (3 S-units).

This is an unpleasant fact of life, but one that must be faced. A receiver in this price class usually has two tuned circuits (r-f and mixer) preceding the i-f stages. It is up to these tuned circuits to separate the real signal and the image signal, which are separated by 910 kilocycles. Two tuned circuits can do a pretty good job of separation at a frequency of, say 4,500 kilocycles. The *ratio of separation* to that of the resonant frequency is 910/4500, or 20.2%. When the circuits are tuned to 30,000 kilocycles the ratio of separation drops to 910/30,000, or only 3.03%. Two tuned circuits, such as the ones used in receivers of this type just cannot offer any degree of discrimination to two frequencies that differ by such a small percentage. As a result, the image problem at 10 meters is bothersome. It can be seen that the degree of image rejection is proportional to the ratio of the received signal to the image frequency, which is also proportional to the ratio of the received signal to the intermediate frequency of the receiver. Generally speaking, when commercial grade components are used, image interference becomes a problem above 10 mc in a receiver having a 455 kc intermediate frequency amplifier and only one r-f stage.

What to Do?

There are several solutions to the image problem. The first and least expensive is to add an additional stage of r-f amplification to the receiver. An extra tuned circuit or two will do wonders to improve the S/I ratio. Some of the more expensive receivers have two r-f stages to help overcome the image problem. The addition of an extra stage, however, is a "brute force" solution to the problem. A more subtle approach is to raise the intermediate frequency to increase the ratio of separation figure. An intermediate frequency of 3,000 kilocycles will provide a ratio of 20% at 30 mc and will increase the S/I ratio enormously. An i-f amplifier operating at this frequency has very poor selectivity and low gain, so it is necessary to use a second mixer tube to convert from this intermediate frequency down to a lower frequency to pick up gain and selectivity. A receiver that accomplishes these functions is called a *double conversion* receiver, and its outstanding attribute is relative freedom from bothersome image signals.

Another solution is to employ a converter with your receiver. The combination of receiver-plus-converter is equivalent to a double conversion receiver in that it combines good image rejection and high selectivity. Converters are often used with high quality communications receivers to extend their range above 30 mc.

An excellent check for receiver sensitivity is to remove the antenna (repeaking the antenna trimmer if necessary) and compare the set noise with and without the antenna. If the receiver can "hear" the atmospheric and antenna noise, the internal noise level of the receiver is low enough for weak-signal reception. In any event, the use of a *good* receiving antenna will improve the performance of even a relatively "flat" receiver.

For the amateur or SWL who already owns a receiver that is subject to image interference, an external, add-on preselector will do much to overcome this problem, and at the same time will provide increased sensitivity over the high frequency portion of the spectrum.

CHAPTER 6

DXing the Frequencies Above 30 Mc

There's a whole new world of radio above 30 mc! Most SWLs have heard of CB radio and they know that their local police and fire departments have radios in their mobile equipment. However, it is only recently that DX listening on the frequencies above 30 mc has become popular. This chapter tells you where the action is, what to listen for, plus all about some of the very interesting VHF DX reception you can enjoy with your TV set, or FM receiver.

So far in this Handbook discussion has centered mainly on frequencies below 30 mc. But the radio spectrum does not end there! TV broadcasting takes place between 54 mc and 890 mc. FM broadcast stations are located between 88 mc and 108 mc. Police and fire departments, forestry services, trucking, taxi, construction companies and telephone utilities are but a few of the occupants of the *Public Service* radio bands located between 30-50 mc, 150-178 mc and 450-470 mc. In addition, a new public service band has recently been authorized near 970 mc. The band between 30 mc and 50 mc is called the *VHF Low Band,* the band between 150 mc and 178 mc is called the *VHF High Band* and the band between 450 mc and 470 mc is called the *UHF Band* (Figure 1).

Interspersed between, and above, these bands are radio amateur bands, government and military channels, radio location (radar) services, weather satellites, and satellites that relay radio and TV programs, as well as telephone conversations, overseas.

CHARACTERISTICS OF THE VHF AND UHF BANDS

The common denominators of the radio spectrum above 30 mc are its reliability over short distances, freedom from static and the vast amount of spectrum space in it. As shown in Figure 2 (and also in Figure 2 of Chapter 2), under normal propagation conditions, radio signals above 30 mc are rarely reflected back to earth via the ionosphere, therefore their reliable ground-wave range is seldom in excess of 100 miles. However, this limited range is no handicap. The primary service area of TV and FM broadcasting stations is seldom over 50 miles. Furthermore, police and fire departments and similar organiza-

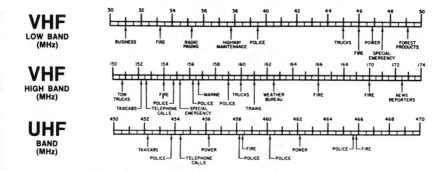

Fig. 1 The Public Service Bands in the VHF and UHF spectrum. Special FM receivers are available that tune these bands. Police, fire departments, forestry services, trucking, taxi, public utilities and emergency services can be heard in all parts of the country. Interspersed between, and above, these bands are aviation and military channels, as well as radio amateurs.

tions, which use radio for short-range communication with their mobile units, are just as well pleased that their transmissions are not broadcast far and wide. Finally, the limited radio range permits the duplication of frequency assignments every few hundred miles across the country without interference between users.

The vast amount of radio spectrum space available above 30 mc is illustrated by the fact that the entire radio spectrum *below* 30 mc is only 30 mc wide, while the spectrum between 30 mc and 1000 mc (only a small slice of the total VHF and UHF spectrum) is 970 mc — over 32 times as wide! This is of great advantage as many types of radio transmission eat up vast chunks of the radio spectrum. A single TV channel, for example, is over five times as wide as an AM broadcast channel! TV and FM signals require a lot of spectrum space because of all the picture and audio information they contain. FM broadcast signals, moreover, are wider than equivalent AM signals in order to achieve noiseless, high quality reception. The wideband signal of FM is rarely heard below 30 mc simply because there is no spectrum space for such signals. On the other hand, with the exception of some uses of single sideband for long-haul circuits, virtually all voice and music transmitted above 30 mc is via FM.

DX Above 30 Mc

Under average conditions, the normal range of VHF and UHF signals is less than 100 miles. However, by use of very high power transmitters, directional antennas and super-sensitive receivers, the military services have developed a number of reliable VHF circuits with maximum ranges in excess of 1000 miles. Then, too, during the peak years of the 11-year sunspot cycle (see Chapter 2), signals from great distances may occasionally be reflected back to earth from the ionosphere on frequencies up to 100 mc.

More common long distance reception of VHF signals, however, depends upon other modes of transmision than these. VHF transmissions are *not*

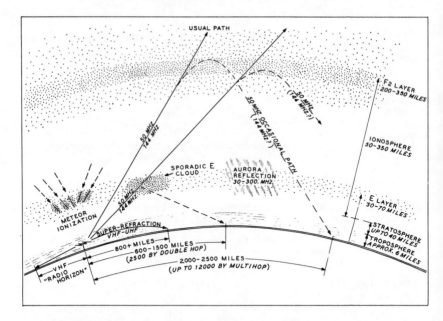

Fig. 2 Atmosphere of the earth is concentrated in a thin layer about 300 miles thick. The ionized layers of air within this span have the ability to reflect electromagnetic energy of certain frequencies. The atmosphere is divided into strata named the troposphere, the stratosphere and the ionosphere. It is in the latter region that radio reflection at the higher frequencies takes place.

limited to line of sight all the time and the listener who is aware of the radio propagation mode involved in long distance VHF reception can have exciting times receiving long distance TV pictures and FM stations. Two propagation modes in the earth's atmosphere accomplish most of this and they are called *sporadic-E skip* and *tropospheric (tropo) skip*.

SPORADIC-E (Es) PROPAGATION

While the ionosphere reflects high frequency radio signals, it has little direct influence on frequencies much above 100 mc. The highest frequency reflected back to earth by the ionosphere is termed the *maximum usable frequency* (MUF), but this does not imply that frequencies above the MUF cannot be used for long distance communication. Sporadic-E propagation is one transmission mode that functions well above the MUF and is thought to be brought about through the presence of small, highly ionized patches of the normal E-layer of the ionosphere at heights of 35 to 60 miles above the earth. Propagation by reflection of radio signals from these small spots in the ionosphere is responsible for the greatest percentage of VHF long distance communication. In the U.S. sporadic-E propagation occurs most often in the spring and summer months, followed by another minor peak in midwinter (Figure 3). It appears more likely to occur shortly before noon or in the late afternoon.

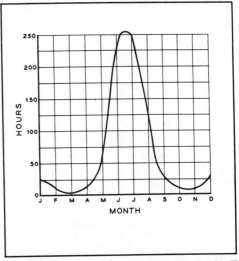

Fig. 3 Sporadic-E openings on the lower VHF bands tend to peak during the summer months. Signals from Mexico and Central America are commonly heard in the U.S. Low-band TV signals are propagated by sporadic-E skip.

The intensely ionized patches of the ionosphere that support sporadic-E appear and disappear with great rapidity, and other patches spring up quickly, so sporadic-E propagation from one general area may last for several hours.

The evidence is not all in as to the highest frequency on which sporadic-E propagation is possible, but the phenomenon decreases rapidly with increasing frequency. It is most common on the radio amateur 6 meter band (50 mc) and on television channel 2 (54 mc).

Sporadic-E skip builds up from the lower frequencies, reaching the lower TV channels and occasionally rising as high as TV channel 6. Reception of the lower TV channels during a sporadic-E propagation opening provides reception up to about 1000 miles. Reception of sporadic-E signals below 500 miles is rare, and the upper distance for this type of skip is about 1500 miles.

On some occasions, double-hop sporadic-E propagation may be observed, caused by two ionized patches between the listener and the station. This permits reception of TV signals up to 2500 miles away. This double skip is much more likely to occur on channel 2 than on the higher channels.

The best way to get started in sporadic-E long distance reception is to leave your TV set tuned to channel 2 or 3 (whichever is not used in your area) and watch for a picture during the months of maximum Es propagation. The picture you see might be extremely strong and clear, or it may fade badly, depending upon propagation conditions. A listing of channel 2 and 3 stations in the U.S., Canada and Mexico is a big help, and you'll find that the north-south path seems to be more prevalent during the summer months. Some TV DXers in the southern part of the U.S. have picked up YSR-TV in San Salvador, El Salvador, on channel 2 with a good quality picture. That's *real* TV DX for you!

TROPOSPHERIC PROPAGATION

The VHF radio wave may be reflected back to earth in the *troposphere*, or "weather layer" of the atmosphere, which extends from sea level to a height of

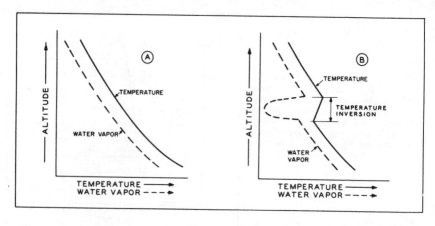

Fig. 4 Long distance tropospheric propagation takes place because of a temperature inversion. The normal temperature and water vapor content of the air decreases with altitude (A). The refractive index of the atmosphere can produce inversion areas (B), showing an abrupt break in water vapor content. If the inversion is pronounced, the resulting bending of the radio wave will follow the curvature of the earth. Atmospheric ducts can propagate VHF signals over distances in excess of 2500 miles.

about six miles. The troposphere is the home of the winds, storms, and rains that continually alter and erode the surface of the earth. Its temperature normally decreases about 20 degrees (Fahrenheit) per mile of altitude, reaching a minimum value of around −58 degrees F. at the upper limit of the region. Meteorological changes in the troposphere are responsible for many interesting VHF radio conditions discussed in this chapter.

Temperature Inversions

Changes in the normal atmosphere affect its refractive index and alter the communication range of VHF waves. For example, after a hot day, a cool evening breeze may blow in from a nearby body of water, forcing the warm air upward. Or, in a change of weather patterns, a large mass of warm tropical air may ride in over surface air. The result is an atmospheric *temperature inversion*, as shown in Figure 4. If the temperature rise reaches 2.8 degrees (Centigrade) per 1000 feet of height, the path of a VHF signal traveling through the atmosphere will be refracted just enough to match the curvature of the earth. When an inversion occurs near the ground or covers only a limited area, the increase in VHF radio range may be less than 150 miles. But when the inversion occurs at a height of several thousand feet and extends over a wide area, the increase in range may be several hundred miles.

Temperature inversions affect all radio frequencies, but the effect increases with frequency. Instances of TV reception between the U.S. mainland and Hawaii have occurred, it is believed, by a form of temperature inversion that provides an atmospheric duct that acts much in the manner of a "radio hose", propagating the VHF signals over distances in excess of 2500 miles.

Temperature inversions occur almost every evening along the Atlantic,

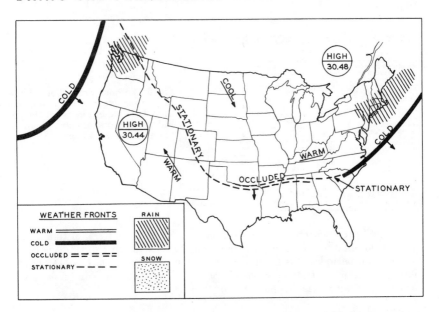

Fig. 5 Temperature inversion forms along a stationary air front where cool high pressure system meets warmer air. During the summer months and into autumn when air movements are slow, it is possible for a sharp inversion to form along a stationary front at the junction of the air masses, and to extend for 800 miles or more. Inversions occur frequently along coastal areas bordering large bodies of water and result from onshore movement of humid air.

Pacific and Gulf coasts of the U.S. during periods when warm, daytime off-shore breezes reverse as the sun goes down, and cool air blows in from the sea. Under these conditions, channel 2 and 3 TV signals along the entire coast can be heard, often in a jumble of sight and sound. Inland, the most spectacular effects take place in the fall months when warm, hazy, calm days are followed by cool nights, when slow, easterly-moving masses of cool Pacific air meet warm Gulf air. Reports of TV reception up to 1400 miles have been noted under such conditions. Weather reports and weather maps help spot weather conditions favorable for extended tropospheric DX reception. Look especially for slow moving highs followed by cold fronts (Figure 5).

Fog, smog and haze are also indications of temperature inversions. And proving that there may be some good in almost anything, when newspapers and radio and TV stations are reporting widespread air-pollution alerts, they are also saying indirectly that extended VHF tropospheric DX should be good in the same areas. Heavy, warm upper air that traps the air pollutants and holds them close to the earth seems to do the same thing for VHF signals. Finally, the rising sun warms the upper air before it warms the surface air often providing better extended-tropospheric VHF propagation conditions than when those conditions occur in the evening hours.

Tropospheric reception is best on the higher TV channels, and on the UHF channels, and poorest on the lower channels. Sometimes during the fall and spring, TV stations from the tropics blanket the entire Gulf coast as far inland as 300 miles, for days at a time.

SPORADIC METEORS	VISUAL MAGNITUDE	WEIGHT, GRAMS	DIAM., CM	ESTIMATED NUMBER SWEPT UP BY EARTH EACH DAY
PARTICLES WHICH REACH GROUND BEFORE BURNING UP	-12.5	10,000	16	10
PARTICLES WHICH BURN COMPLETELY IN UPPER ATMOSPHERE	-10	1000	8	100
	-7.5	100	4	1000
	-5	10	1.6	10,000
	-2.5	1	.8	100,000
	0	.1	.4	1 MILLION
	2.5	.01	.16	10 MILLION
	5	.001	.08	100 MILLION
SMALLEST PARTICLES DETECTABLE BY RADAR ⟶	7.5	.0001	.04	1 BILLION
	10	.00001	.016	10 BILLION

Fig. 6 Largest proportion of meteors reaching the earth are less than 0.016 cm in diameter. Over 12 billion meteors are swept up by the earth each 24 hours.

"Tropo" propagation provides an excellent TV picture, weak at times, but quite steady and provides many happy hours of DX hunting during the peak propagation periods. This form of propagation provides good FM DX reception, too, and many stations in the 88 mc to 108 mc FM band can be received over long distances via "tropo" propagation.

METEOR PROPAGATION

For many years, it was commonly thought that outer space was an empty void with nothing between the planets and the stars. Meteors have been observed flashing through the night-time skies from the start of recorded history but were assumed to be comparatively few in number. Today, we know the solar system contains untold billions of meteors and many of these reach our earth. Most are too small to be seen on their fiery trips, a small percentage are large enough to be seen as they burn up in the atmosphere, and a very few of the latter strike the earth before burning up. It is now known that meteors are also a day-time phenomenon, although they cannot be easily observed.

There are two types of meteors. The most common type is very sporadic, arriving in view from random directions and traveling over a wide range of

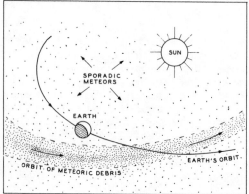

Fig. 7 Earth cuts through a stream of meteor debris in path of comet. Width of debris orbit may require several days for earth to move through the path.

| NAME OF SHOWER | | DATE OF MAXIMUM | RADIANT COORDINATES | | AVERAGE HOURLY RATE * | VELOCITY KM/SEC. |
			RIGHT ASCENSION	DECLINATION		
NIGHT TIME	QUADRANTIDS [1]	JAN. 3	230°	+52°	35-45	39
	LYRIDS [1]	APRIL 21	270	+33	8-12	51
	η-AQUARIDS [1]	MAY 6	338	+3	12	66
DAY TIME SHOWERS	PISCIDS	MAY 7-13	26	+25	30	—
	O-CETIDS [1]	MAY 21	30	-3	20	—
	ζ-PERSEIDS [1]	JUNE 3	61.5	+24.4	40	28.8
	ARIETIDS [1]	JUNE 2-14	44.3	+22.6	60	37.6
	54-PERSEIDS	JUNE 25	68	+33	50	—
	β-TAURIDS [1]	JULY 2	86.2	+18.7	30	31.5
	Q-ORIONIDS	JULY 12	87	+11	50	—
	ν-GEMINIDS	JULY 12	98	+21	60	—
	λ-GEMINIDS	JULY 12	111	+15	32	—
	δ-AURIGIDS	JULY 25	87	+38	20	—
NIGHT TIME	δ-AQUARIDS [1]	JULY 28	339	-11	10-22	50
	PERSEIDS [1]	AUG. 10-14	47	+58	50	61
	GIACOBINIDS [2]	OCT. 9	262	+54	VARIES	20
	ORIONIDS [1]	OCT. 20-23	96	+15	15-30	68
	TAURIDS [1]	NOV. 3-10	55	+15	10-16	27
	LEONIDS	NOV. 14	25	+45	VARIES	22
	LEONIDS [1]	NOV. 16-17	152	+22	12	72
	GEMINIDS [1]	DEC. 13-14	113	+32	60-70	35
	URSIDS [1]	DEC. 22	207	+77	13	38

1 —ANNUAL RECURRING SHOWERS.
2 —THESE SHOWERS HAVE PRODUCED TREMENDOUS DISPLAYS IN THE PAST, ALTHOUGH IN RECENT YEARS THEIR HOURLY RATE HAS BEEN QUITE SMALL.
* —HOURLY RATE OF VISIBLE TRAILS FROM ONE OBSERVATION POST.

Fig. 8 Meteor showers of interest to VHF listeners are listed above. The spring showers tend to peak between midnight and 6 a.m., and again near noon. Meteor activity tends to build up and drop off slowly so DXers usually listen a few days either side of the peak period.

velocities. Figure 6 lists them according to mass, size and approximate number that enter the earth's orbit per day. The second type appears when the earth sweeps through a meteor stream (Figure 7). These streams are believed to be the debris that follows a comet as it orbits the sun. Figure 8 tabulates these *meteor showers* and shows how they peak during June, July and August.

As a meteor disintegrates in its path across the sky, the process produces a burst of ionization around it. The ionization appears as a cylindrical column around the particle, expanding by diffusion through the rarified atmosphere. The ionized atmosphere is sufficiently large in many cases to affect a VHF signal momentarily. But the ionization produced by a stream of meteors is nearly continuous and it supports short bursts of VHF communication. It is these bursts — occasionally up to 40 seconds duration — that produce excep-

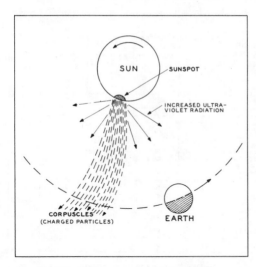

Fig. 9 Sunspot storm bombards earth with charged corpuscles creating ionospheric chaos. The MUF radio "blackout" is sometimes avoided by earth passing ahead of corpuscular cloud, as shown here.

tional VHF DX reception. TV signals propagated by meteor scatter can be seen and identified, especially if the station in question is running a test pattern. Channel 2 and 3 signals have been logged up to a distance of about 1200 miles via meteor scatter.

AURORA PROPAGATION

Among the forms of extended VHF propagation that excites listeners and irritates commercial VHF users is *aurora reflection*. The generally accepted theory regarding the formation of visible *Aurora Borealis* displays around the north magnetic pole, and the *Aurora Australis* around the south magnetic pole, is that they result from the sun emitting masses of hot, ionized gasses, especially after solar flares (Figure 9). As these solar emissions flow toward the earth, they are split by the earth's magnetic field and follow the magnetic field lines to the other side of the earth; here they concentrate around the magnetic poles,

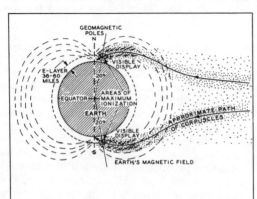

Fig. 10 Maximum aurora display is concentrated in a broad belt near 70 degrees latitude from each geomagnetic pole. Visible ionization occurs at a height of 60 to 70 miles in the E-layer of the ionosphere.

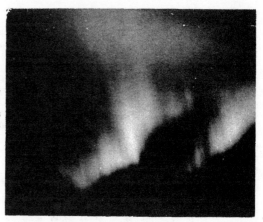

Fig. 11 Aurora display may signify east-west DX paths are open on VHF bands. Stations can be heard up to 800 miles distance via aurora skip.

as illustrated in Figure 10. At the poles, the streams of energy from the sun strike the atmosphere at a height of 60 to 70 miles and produce the vivid displays so often seen in the polar skies.

The aurora displays are almost constantly visible around the magnetic poles (Figure 11). Extremely strong aurora displays have occasionally been seen as far south as Atlanta, Georgia. But, because the magnetic north pole is located near Thule, Greenland, western areas of the states see fewer auroras than do corresponding eastern areas. Figure 12 gives the general picture.

Reflection of VHF signals from the aurora displays seems to take place at a height of about 60 miles and most aurora propagation takes place in a generally east-west direction over a distance of several hundred miles out to about 1200 miles on rare occasions. The aurora-reflected signal wavers and a TV picture flickers badly, making video identification difficult. Aurora propagation occurs most frequently on channels 2 and 3, but is occasionally present on higher

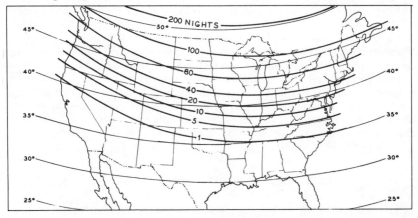

Fig. 12 Aurora display is most prevalent at northern latitudes, but can be seen on occasion as far south as New Mexico or Arkansas. Aurora reflects VHF signals which are modulated by rapid oscillation of the aurora, resulting in a characteristic "growl" or "hiss" superimposed on the signal.

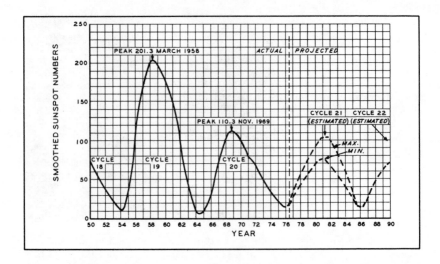

Fig. 13 Sunspot cycle repeats itself approximately every 11 years. During the peaks of the cycle when the solar spots are most numerous, the maximum usable frequency tends to average quite a bit higher than during periods of minimum sunspot activity. VHF propagation by ionospheric reflection may occur during peak years. Exceptional VHF DX was logged during peak of 1958.

channels. It is most frequent near the summer and winter equinoxes in the early morning and evening hours, but it also occurs in other months and at other times.

TRANSEQUATORIAL PROPAGATION

First observed by radio amateurs in 1957, *transequatorial propagation* (T-E) provides a signal path in areas located in belts centered approximately 2500 miles on either side of the geomagnetic equator. It is quite prevalent in the southern parts of the United States in the late afternoon and early evening hours of the spring and fall. Transequatorial propagation seems to occur as high as 85 mc, thus taking in the amateur 6 meter band and the low-band TV channels. Along the southern border of the U.S., TV signals can often be heard by T-E "scatter" down through Central America and corresponding regions south of the Equator. Signals propagated by this mode have a characteristic flutter which tends to distort the audio in most instances. The TV picture, moreover, is badly distorted and torn.

IONOSPHERIC PROPAGATION VIA THE F2-LAYER

The reflective ability of the ionosphere is greatly affected by the *sunspot cycle*. Over an average period of 11 years, the observed number of spots on the sun (thought to be fierce storms) increases from a minimum value to a maximum and back to a minimum, and the cycle starts over again (Figure 13). As the sunspot count waxes and wanes, so do various emanations from the sun.

The maximum radio frequency that will be reflected from the ionosphere also varies with the sunspot cycle. In 1958, when the smoothed sunspot count reached the highest value ever recorded, the maximum usable frequency (MUF) for ionospheric propagation exceeded 70 mc. During a sunspot minimum, the MUF is often less than 30 mc. Complicating the picture is the fact that no two solar cycles are exactly the same. Both the 1947 and 1969 sunspot cycle peaks were lower than the 1958 peak but were still high enough to support long distance communication as high as 60 mc on good days.

During periods of high sunspot activity, spectacular transatlantic television DX is possible with F2 propagation. While the sunspot cycle will not reach a new peak until about 1980, short periods of erratic F2 "skip" are possible during spring and fall months. Thus, European viewers can occasionally catch glimpses of U.S. television channel 2, and American viewers can pull in the British Broadcasting Corporation TV signals (audio) on 41.5 mc and the French TV audio signals on 41.25 mc. Both of these signals are AM, unlike the American signals, which are FM. Receiving the picture transmissions, however, is difficult as the European stations transmit to different technical standards. On the west coast of the United States, TV signals from Hawaii, Japan and Korea have been noted on occasions.

DX TV RECEPTION

Are you interested in seeing TV signals direct from faraway places? You can do it with your TV receiver. The key to good long distance TV reception is your antenna. You'll need a good, high gain TV antenna tuned to the low band (channels 2 through 4) mounted high and in the clear. A TV rotator is a "must" and the kind that provides continuous rotation, rather than the type that moves in six degree steps, is preferred. An antenna preamplifier is a great help, as it builds up the weak signals so that they can be better identified. A complete directory of all the important radio and TV stations in the world can be found in *World Radio TV Handbook*, available from Billboard Publications, Inc., One Astor Plaza, New York, NY 10036.

DX FM RECEPTION

The casual FM listener is often amazed at the distant stations he can hear on his FM receiver using an indoor antenna. However, the serious DX listener requires a good FM antenna mounted high and in the clear. A special FM antenna should be used, and not a combination FM-TV antenna which, at best, is a compromise for both types of reception. Many good, powerful FM receiving antennas are available from radio distributors and the use of such a device, plus a good antenna rotator, is highly recommended.

One problem the FM DXer has is receiver overload from strong, local FM signals. The rotary antenna helps in this respect, as it may be aimed away from the local station, thus dropping its strength. Some FM receivers are more sensitive and resistive to overload than others and a prospective buyer should check the various consumer magazines which often have complete technical reviews of FM receivers.

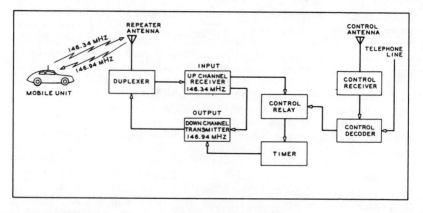

Fig. 14 VHF amateur repeater receives and amplifies signals on one channel and repeats them on another channel. In this example, the repeater input channel is 146.34 mc and the output is 146.94 mc. The repeater system is turned on and off by the user. When the repeater "hears" a signal on the input frequency, it is activated until the signal goes off the air. Repeater stations are also used in the Public Service bands to extend the range of the various mobile units in a particular location.

A complete list of FM stations is given in the *FM Atlas and Station Directory*, available from FM Atlas Co., Box 24D, Adolph, Minnesota 55701.

DXing the VHF Amateur Bands

A tremendous amount of ham activity takes place in the VHF region. The most active of the amateur VHF bands are 50-54 mc, 144-148 mc and 220-225 mc. At present, most activity on them is FM transmission through *repeater stations* located in most large cities. The repeater is an automatic relay station that gives low power mobile ham stations and hand-held "walkie-talkies" the range of a high power, fixed station (Figure 14). Groups of radio amateurs converse among themselves, using a common repeater much in the manner of a party line telephone! Most communities have one or more repeater stations and they can be copied over long distances when a good, amateur-type FM receiver is used.

DXing the Public Service Bands

As mentioned earlier in this chapter, three Public Service bands exist, called the *Low Band,* the *High Band* and the *UHF Band.* Low Band (30-50 mc) signals can usually be heard from greater distances than either High Band (152-178 mc) or UHF Band (450-470 mc).

A lot of interesting communications goes on in these bands. In almost every community there are police, fire, land transportation and industrial radio stations you can hear. In addition, the sheriff's department, the taxicab company, your hospital, the National Weather Stations and ship-to-shore communications fill the band 24 hours a day. These stations are not on the air continuously, but pop on and off with short communications between the base, or control, station and the mobile stations. The transmisions are FM and can be logged with a scanning *monitor receiver* that covers one, or more, of the public service bands.

Interspersed between and above the public service bands are government and military channels, radio location (radar) devices, weather satellites and satellites that relay radio and TV programs, and telephone conversations, overseas. Most of these signals are transmitted on a narrow beam and are very difficult to receive and interpret and, as a result, most of the VHF DXing goes on in the more easily received Public Service bands.

Specialized VHF Reception

One of the most dramatic, and secret, shortwave listening operations is carried on by the U.S. intelligence groups using space satellites which crisscross over foreign countries in outer space gathering radio and photographic intelligence data. *Ferret satellites,* for instance, record radio signals on many different frequencies while over foreign lands, and on command from a U.S. ground station, play the signals back so they can be recorded and analyzed. These satellites transmit on extremely high frequencies in the UHF range and are virtually impossible for the average listener to copy.

Vela satellites packed with sensitive instruments can detect nuclear explosions in outer space and anywhere on earth. *Photograph Reconnaisance satellites* take amazingly clear pictures of military installations around the world for intelligence analysis. The photo package can be transmitted back to earth by UHF radio, or jettisoned at a predetermined spot and caught in mid-air by a specially equipped aircraft manned by skilled crews.

These radio activities, and others like them, take place every day but due to the sophisticated transmission techniques, the unusually high frequencies used, and the short span of transmission times, such signals are rarely heard by the casual listener.

Citizens Band (CB) DX Listening

The first of the bands on the very edge of the HF/VHF spectrum is the 11 meter *Citizens Band.* The Citizens Radio Service was established in 1958 as a personal radio service (not amateur radio) and up to the present has grown to over 1 million licensees. CB radio, as it is commonly known, is used by small businesses and by individuals as originally intended, but the greatest use is for personal pleasure and "hobby-style" conversations, something that the original concept did not contemplate.

A large portion of CB radio operation is, at present, illegal. That is, it is conducted by unlicensed stations which sign fictitious calls. In the larger cities, by far the greater proportion of stations heard fall in this category.

CB stations may be either fixed or mobile and many CB operators have elaborate installations in their autos, trucks or recreation vehicles. Interstate truckers, in particular, are enthusiastic users of CB radio.

In any event, CB radio is growing in popularity and it is interesting to listen to the CB band to "observe the action." Various CB monitor receivers are available at a modest price, most of them imported from the Orient. A simple ground plane antenna, also available at any CB radio store, provides good listening for local communications.

The observant listener will quickly note that many CBers talk in their own private coded language and it often takes a quick ear to interpret what one hears. Large numbers of CB clubs across the United States are ready to assist the newcomer to this novel, interesting and controversial aspect of VHF radio communication.

INTERPLANETARY COMMUNICATIONS

It has been pointed out that millions of stars resemble our sun and that chances are good that planets may exist close enough to such stars to receive the warmth necessary for life. Based upon this assumption, several attempts are being made to intercept radio signals from other worlds. The search is for steady signals that, because of their narrow frequency band, definite rhythm or other distinct properties seem to carry information.

The first attempt was in 1960 in which a huge parabolic "dish" antenna of the *National Radio Astronomy Observatory* in West Virginia monitored two nearby stars on what then seemed the logical frequency for making contact. No signals of distant origin were observed. In 1968, Russian scientists scanned 12 nearby stars similar in type to our sun for fluctuating signals at various frequencies. Again, the results were negative. The tests were repeated with more sensitive equipment, using twin reception points, then finally using seven reception points, with no positive results.

By 1972 it was concluded that the power required for radio transmission from nearby suns to the earth would take too much energy and the supposition that other civilizations were sending signals to us was quite remote — but possible.

A new approach was contemplated, that of eavesdropping on possible radio and microwave transmissions that were not aimed directly at us. This could be done, particularly at wavelengths that have less radio noise than others.

EAVESDROPPING ON OTHER WORLDS

Underway at present is a study to determine if it is possible to eavesdrop on distant civilizations, if any exist within 100 light years of the earth. A special antenna array is believed able to do the job. It will consist of 10,000 dish-shaped antennas, each 100 feet in diameter, spread over an area 10 to 20 miles wide! It is expected that such a gigantic antenna could detect "radio leakage" from a technological civilization up to 100 light years away. Within this distance, there are some 10,000 stars, many of which presumably have planets orbiting them.

When this project is active, it will certainly be the most ambitious and complex SWL activity the world has ever seen. Unfortunately, the antennas and equipment required put this type of SWL activity beyond the ability of individuals.

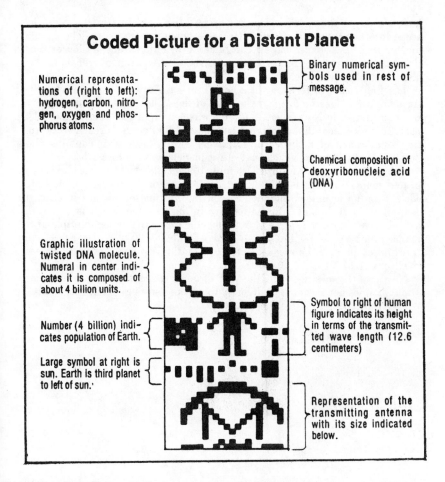

Coded Picture for a Distant Planet

Numerical representations of (right to left): hydrogen, carbon, nitrogen, oxygen and phosphorus atoms.

Binary numerical symbols used in rest of message.

Chemical composition of deoxyribonucleic acid (DNA)

Graphic illustration of twisted DNA molecule. Numeral in center indicates it is composed of about 4 billion units.

Number (4 billion) indicates population of Earth.

Large symbol at right is sun. Earth is third planet to left of sun.

Symbol to right of human figure indicates its height in terms of the transmitted wave length (12.6 centimeters)

Representation of the transmitting antenna with its size indicated below.

Fig. 15   A coded message has been sent into space that gives a positive indication of life on earth. The message consists of 1,679 "bits" of information which can be reconstructed into this picture. The message will take 24,000 years to reach its destination at the edge of the Milky Way.

In addition to listening for signs of intelligent life, the huge radio telescope would be able to listen out to the fringes of the universe, perhaps resolving problems as to its origin and destiny.

TRANSMITTING TO OTHER WORLDS

A companion program that would utilize much of the same equipment is designed to send a coded message into space that could be deciphered by a computer, giving a positive indication of life on Earth. These transmissions have already commenced, using the giant "dish" antenna of the radio tele-scope located at Arecibo, Puerto Rico as a temporary measure. The antenna, located in a bowl-shaped valley, can be used for either transmission or recep-tion of microwave signals from far out in space. A powerful transmitter was also available at this site.

The first step was to transmit a coded message toward a global cluster of stars known as *Messier 13* near the edge of the Milky Way. The first message was transmitted in November, 1974 on a wavelength of 12.6 centimeters (2381 mc). It is estimated that the signal will take 24,000 years to reach its destina-tion! This particular cluster of stars was chosen because it contains about 300,000 stars, some of which may have planets similar to earth.

The coded message (Figure 15) took 169 seconds to transmit and was re-peated many times. It is printed out as 73 lines of 23 message units (bits) each, forming an image intended to convey information about life on earth. A total of 1,679 bits of information are in the message and it is hoped that any observer in outer space will note the clue that 1,679 is the multiple of two prime numbers — 73 and 23 — and will deduce that an image is being transmitted that can be reconstructed by printing the message as 73 consecu-tive lines of 23 bits.

Now that the message is on the way in outer space, traveling at a speed of 186,000 miles per second, it will be up to our ancestors to determine if a reply is ever received!

CHAPTER VII

All About VHF Receivers

VHF receivers differ in important details from high frequency receivers. This chapter discusses some of the differences and explains how VHF receivers work. Written in nontechnical language, the mysteries of scanning receivers, squelch circuits, automatic frequency control, synthesizers and other exotic subjects relating to VHF reception are discussed.

Because of the extreme width of the radio spectrum above 30 mc and the widely different characteristics of receivers for the different services, it is impractical to design a single receiver to cover all of the services in this region. All VHF receivers, however, have some common circuitry that differs from the HF receivers discussed earlier in this Handbook. This chapter covers the VHF receivers in some detail and explains the important points of these interesting devices.

The great majority of services in the VHF spectrum employ *frequency modulation* (FM) and thus most receivers use this mode to achieve relatively noise-free reception.

VHF RECEIVER NOISE

Generally speaking, the VHF receiver has a very sensitive rf amplifier stage and is a double conversion superheterodyne of the type discussed in Chapter 2. It is designed to have a very low internal noise level so that the weakest signals may be heard. In every receiver a random signal voltage exists even when no meaningful signal is being received. This voltage is termed *noise* and in addition to being generated within the receiver, noise can be picked up by the antenna from various external noise sources. The higher the receiver gain, the higher the unwanted noise level; every receiver is ultimately noise-limited as far as absolute sensitivity is concerned.

Internal receiver noise is usually masked at the lower frequencies by the high level of external noise picked up by the antenna. The level of external

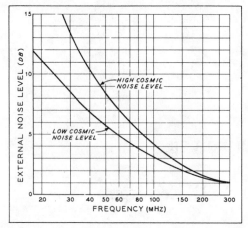

Fig. 1 Cosmic radio noise decreases as the frequency increases. The sky has many sources of radio energy. Internal receiver noise is usually quite low at the lower frequencies, rising above 100 MHz. It is the limiting factor in most VHF receivers.

noise drops gradually as the frequency of reception is increased until in the 50 mc region it is quite low, as illustrated in Figure 1. Internal receiver noise, on the other hand, is minor at the lower frequencies, becoming more important above 100 mc (Figure 2). At higher frequencies the internal noise of a typical receiver usually forms a "floor" or minimum level beneath which it is difficult to identify signals. By proper design, internal receiver noise can be reduced to a minimum, permitting reception of very weak VHF signals.

Most receiver noise is caused by *thermal agitation noise,* or the noise created by a random motion of electrons in the components. It exists in all parts of the receiver, but the greatest portion is generated in the input stage of the receiver, at the point the received signal is the weakest. The term *noise figure*

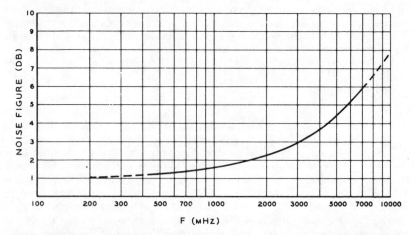

Fig. 2 Typical noise figure for sensitive receiver rises from about 1.2 decibels below 450 MHz to near 6 decibels in UHF range. Most low cost VHF receivers exhibit noise figures 3 to 5 decibels worse than this. A noise figure of 3 decibels for a VHF scanning receiver is very good. A low noise figure below about 100 MHz is not required in most cases, as cosmic and man-made external noise determines ultimate receiver sensitivity.

is used to define the noise power output of the receiver compared to a perfect, noiseless receiver. The noise figure is expressed in decibels and good low-noise VHF receivers often have a noise figure that is only one or two decibels worse than the "perfect" receiver.

External noise is quite different in the VHF spectrum than in the HF spectrum. Man-made noise and atmospheric noise tend to decrease with increasing frequency and are usually quite low in the VHF region. One source of VHF noise comes from the sun and the large number of radio stars located along the galactic plane. *Galactic noise* is largely blocked out below 20 mc by atmospheric noise and ionospheric absorption, but is noticeable in the VHF region. When a high gain beam antenna is aimed at the sun, for example, a sensitive receiver will indicate a loud, hissing sound, which is radio noise coming from the sun.

RECEIVER CIRCUITRY

In the past decade, the transistor has replaced the vacuum tube in VHF receiving equipment and in low power VHF transmitters. Only in relatively high power applications does the vacuum tube compete with the transistor in the ever-changing world of VHF radio. In addition, modern VHF receivers are *channelized*, that is, they are not continuous tuning as are most shortwave receivers but jump from channel to channel, much in the manner of a television receiver. The typical VHF receiver, moreover, is crystal controlled to achieve a high order of frequency stability.

The main point of difference between the HF receiver and the VHF receiver, however, is that the latter is designed for FM reception. *Frequency modulation* (FM) provides a system which rejects most man-made noise and disturbances of natural origin, thus it promises a virtually noise-free communication circuit.

Frequency modulation is a widely used technique to modulate a radio signal. The audio portion of all U.S. TV signals is transmitted by FM, as are the high fidelity broadcasts in the FM band. VHF radio amateurs, as well, use FM as a principal mode of communication.

THE FM RECEIVER

The FM receiver differs from the common AM receiver in several important ways. First of all, and most important, the FM receiver has a critical sensitivity *threshold level*, usually very low, above which signals quiet the background noise and are heard with dramatic clarity, as compared to an AM signal received on an AM receiver. In addition, the modern FM receiver is equipped with a *squelch* circuit that disables the loudspeaker when no signals are being received. As a result, the FM receiver can provide nearly noise-free reception for point-to-point VHF operation, and the design of such devices has reached a high degree of proficiency.

A representative "front end" circuit of a VHF receiver is shown in Figure 3. A dual-gate MOSFET is used as an rf amplifier stage (Q1). The incoming signal is applied to one gate of this tiny amplifier and the second gate is used for automatic gain control. Since the receiver covers a restricted tuning range, no coil switching is required. A single gate FET is used as a mixer stage, with

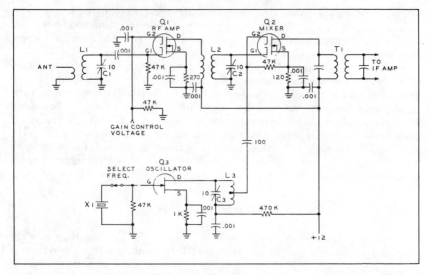

Fig. 3 "Front end" circuitry of typical VHF receiver. Dual-gate MOSFET is used as an r-f amplifier stage (Q1). Signal-gate FET serves as a mixer (Q2). Local oscillator (Q3) is crystal controlled and mixing voltage is applied to the source of Q2. Bipolar transistors may be used in circuits similar to these, but they are more susceptible to overload from strong signals.

the signal of the local oscillator applied to the source element (Q2). Bipolar transistors may also be used in circuits similar to these, but they are more susceptible to overload from strong, nearby signals.

The local oscillator (Q3) in the typical Public Service Band receiver is crystal controlled, using relatively inexpensive, low frequency crystals whose frequency is electronically multiplied to the proper value for mixing purposes, as shown in the diagram.

THE FREQUENCY SYNTHESIZER

Crystal control can become quite expensive when many VHF channels are involved, as one crystal is required for each channel. A *frequency synthesizer* offers the flexibility of a number of crystals and saves money and space (Figure 4). In this example, a single 100 kc crystal is divided down to 10 kc, then multiplied by 59, 60 or 61 to provide a spectrum of many signals around 600 kc (590, 600, 610 kc, etc.). One signal (say, 600 kc) is selected by a suitable filter. A harmonic generator also provides a 7400 kc signal which is then combined in a mixer stage with the 600 kc signal. A resulting signal at 8000 kc (the sum of 7400 kc and 600 kc) appears in the output circuit. By switching the harmonic generator from a multiplication factor of 60 to some other factor (say, 62), the output frequency will shift to 8020 kc, which is then multiplied by 18 to create a 144.36 mc mixing signal.

A multiple crystal synthesizer is shown in Figure 5. Ten crystals provide an output signal in the range of 1100 kc to 2100 kc in 100 kc steps. In conjunction with a harmonic generator and mixer, a number of mixing frequen-

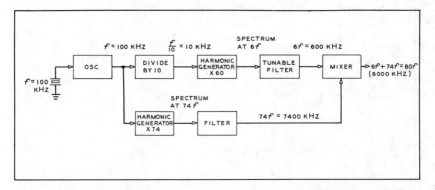

Fig. 4 A box full of crystals can be eliminated by use of a frequency synthesizer which offers the flexibility of a variable frequency oscillator and the stability and accuracy of a crystal oscillator. This synthesizer uses a master 100 kHz crystal to provide a spectrum of signals, 10 kHz apart, at 600 kHz. One signal is selected by a suitable filter and is mixed with a second signal to produce an output signal at 8 MHz. The second signal is derived from the crystal oscillator and a harmonic generator. The output of the harmonic generator is passed through a second filter and the selected frequency of 7400 kHz is fed to the mixer stage. Other circuits may use crystals and multiplication factors that are different from this example.

cies are created. If the 100 kc oscillator is made tunable, moreover, a continuous coverage of the output spectrum can be achieved. Circuits such as these, and others, provide multi-channel capability for VHF reception and transmission at a modest cost.

The I-F Amplifier and Limiter

The *i-f amplifier* of the VHF FM receiver commonly operates at 10.7 mc instead of 455 kc to achieve a passband wide enough to accept the wideband

Fig. 5 Multiple crystal synthesizer uses 10 crystals to provide an output signal in the range of 1100 kHz to 2100 kHz in 100 kHz steps. If the 100 kHz oscillator is made tunable over a narrow range, a continuous coverage of the output spectrum can be achieved.

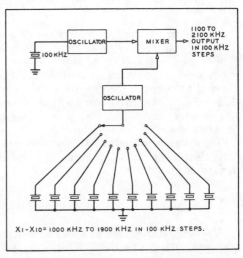

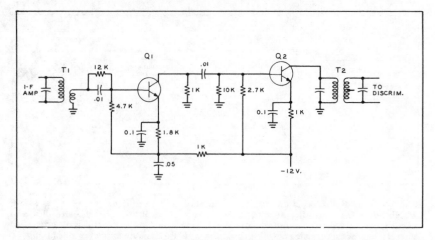

Fig. 6 The limiter stage is used in FM receiver to "wash out" all amplitude variations in the signal. The limiter (Q1, Q2) is a high gain i-f amplifier which overloads easily. It is driven with a large signal and the output signal of the limiter remains relatively constant for wide variations in the amplitude of the input signal. Most noise is a form of amplitude modulation, and noise is suppressed by the limiter stage.

signal and also to improve the image rejection of the receiver.

In order to provide a degree of discrimination against noise and AM signals, a special i-f amplifier stage called a *limiter* is used which "washes out" all amplitude variations on the signal (Figure 6). The limiter is simply a high gain amplifier stage which overloads easily. It is supplied with a large signal from the preceding i-f amplifiers, and the output from the limiter does not change for rather wide variations in the strength of the signal. After limiting, the signal passes to the discriminator, or detector stage.

THE FM DETECTOR

The "heart" of the FM receiver is a device for converting frequency modulation into an audio signal. The simplest circuit to do this, and one that is widely used, is the *discriminator*, shown in Figure 7. This is essentially two diode detectors connected back-to-back. When tuned to the carrier signal of the FM transmitter, the detector develops no output voltage. As soon as the FM signal moves in frequency with modulation, signal voltages appear across the detectors and an a-c voltage is developed as the signal varies across the input passband of the detector.

The discriminator provides some degree of discrimination against noise and aids the limiter circuit in reducing noise and interference to provide good noise-free reception.

THE SQUELCH CIRCUIT

Most FM receivers use an audio *squelch circuit* to disable the receiver when no signal is being received. When a carrier comes on, the squelch is turned

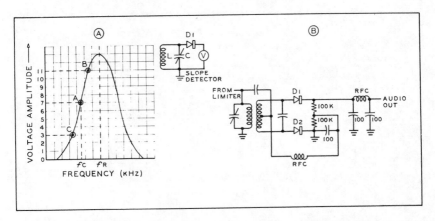

Fig. 7 The FM detector. The slope detector is shown in (A). A carrier signal is tuned in at point A on the selectivity curve and as the frequency of the signal varies from A to B to C, the output signal of the detector varies in strength from 3 to 11 units. A discriminator circuit is shown at (B). This is essentialy two slope detectors connected back-to-back. When tuned to the carrier signal, the detector develops no output. As soon as the signal is modulated, an a-c voltage is developed as the signal varies across the passband of the FM detector.

off and the audio system of the receiver is actuated. More modern FM receivers use a noise operated squelch which monitors the background noise of the receiver. Noise voltage is rectified to produce a squelch action that is stable and independent of the absolute value of either noise or signal (Figure 8).

AUTOMATIC FREQUENCY CONTROL

Because the operating frequencies of a VHF receiver are high, a very small change in the frequency determining circuit will shift the frequency to which the receiver is tuned. This is no problem with a crystal controlled receiver, but a tunable receiver (such as for FM broadcast reception) must be constantly retuned to keep the desired station in the receiver passband. This instability problem is solved with an *automatic frequency control* (AFC) circuit. This consists of an electronic capacitor which is tuned by means of a control voltage developed in the discriminator stage of the receiver. As the receiver drifts off the chosen frequency, the control voltage is applied to the capacitor which tunes the receiver back to the frequency of the incoming signal. A switch permits the AFC circuit to be disconnected while tuning in stations.

THE SCANNING RECEIVER

Continuous tuning receivers are convenient for listeners who are interested in eavesdropping on all signals in a given Public Service Band. Because many transmissions in these bands are of short duration, and because the bands are so wide, the average listener seems to spend most of his time spinning the dial of his receiver between stations that go off the air just as they are tuned in!

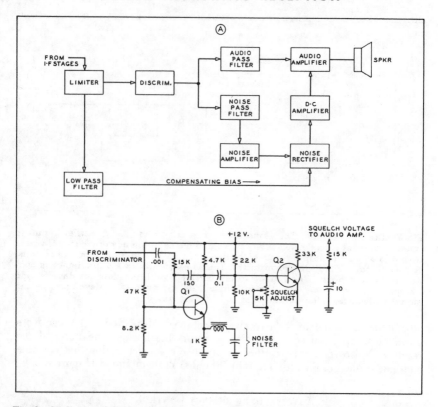

Fig. 8   Audio squelch circuit disables the receiver when no signal is being received. When a carrier comes on, the squelch is turned off and the audio system of the receiver is actuated. In this representative circuit, the noise voltage from the discriminator is filtered and rectified to operate switch transistor Q2. The transistor passes control voltage to audio amplifier. Squelch action is stable and independent of absolute value of either the signal or the noise.

If you are interested in monitoring a limited number of channels in one or more of the Service Bands, a crystal controlled *scanning receiver* is the answer. By using proper crystals in the receiver, the listener is assured that any station in range on the chosen channels will be heard almost as soon as it comes on the air.

The scanning receiver silently samples each channel in the receiver tuning range several times a second. When a signal appears on a channel, the scanner locks on the signal and the receiver squelch circuit opens, permitting the signal to be heard. At the same time, an indicating light on the panel glows to identify the channel being received. A second after the signal goes off the air, the scanner resumes its constant search until another signal is heard. If desired, the receiver may be set to remain locked on one channel, or to skip one or more channels, in each scan by adjustment of panel switches. In addition, some scanning receivers can be adjusted to lock on a priority channel whenever there is any signal on it. Most scanning receivers can be equipped to monitor up to eight channels in one, two or three different bands.

Fig. 9 Typical scanning receiver for home or mobile use. Receiver scans 16 channels in Public Service Band. Receiver samples each channel and when a signal is heard, the receiver locks on the channel and the receiver squelch circuit opens, permitting the signal to be heard. Indicator lights signal channel in use.

The earliest form of scanning receiver was crystal controlled, with a rotary switch driven at low speed by a motor. The switch selected the receiving crystals in sequence, tuning over and over again through the channels. The motor was stopped automatically by the squelch circuit, leaving the receiver tuned to a channel on which a signal was being intercepted.

In a practical, modern scanning receiver, there is neither an electric motor nor a rotary switch. Instead, the crystals are cut in and out of the circuit in sequence by electronic switches which are automatically triggered in the proper sequence. The scanning action is controlled by a sensing system run by an "electronic clock"

In buying a scanning receiver, remember that it comes without frequency control crystals in the majority of cases. The purchaser should know the local channel frequencies in use. The dealer may have the appropriate crystals in stock, or they may have to be ordered from the receiver manufacturer, or a crystal company, by mail.

CHAPTER VIII

Better Antennas for Your Receiver

A receiver is no better than its antenna! Some listeners buy an expensive receiver, hang a hunk of wire on it, and are disappointed at the results they obtain. "Aw, the receiver is no good. Shortwave reception is the bunk," they say. This situation can be avoided if a little care and thought is put into the erection of the receiving antenna. Big dividends in the form of improved reception may be gained with the use of an efficient, well planned antenna, such as one of the various types described in this chapter. Give your receiver and yourself a break! Put up a good antenna for best DX reception!

An *antenna* (or *aerial)* is a device that will capture electromagnetic energy from space and convert it to a movement or drift of electrons. The most common form of antenna is a piece of copper wire strung between two supports. The efficiency of such a simple device is a function of the length of the wire as compared to the length of the radio wave, and the angle at which the radio wave strikes the wire. Every type of radio antenna has directional characteristics causing it to intercept energy better in certain directions than in others.

One end of the antenna wire may be brought into the house and connected directly to the antenna terminal of the receiver, or the antenna may be separated from the receiver and connected to it by a "radio hose" called a *transmission line*, which conducts the energy from the antenna to the receiver with a minimum of loss.

What Is A Good Antenna?

A good antenna is the key to successful shortwave reception. Time and effort spent in making the best antenna installation possible will result in greatly improved reception. No matter what form or type of antenna you use, it must follow some rather fundamental rules, or it will not be worth the time and money required to put it up. Here are these rules:

1—The antenna should be erected as high in the air as possible. Twenty

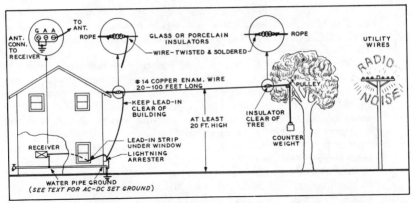

Fig. 1 The single wire antenna shown above is simple and inexpensive to build and will produce good results over the whole shortwave spectrum. The antenna should be erected as high as possible, and at right angles to any nearby power lines. Make sure the lead-in does not touch the gutter pipes.

feet above the ground may be considered to be a minimum height. Some amateur transmitting and receiving antennas are placed eighty or ninety feet in the air to obtain optimum results! Get your antenna as high in the air as you can.

2—The location of the antenna with respect to nearby objects is very important. Telephone lines and power lines exhibit a shielding effect to a nearby antenna. Stucco buildings having wire mesh in the walls are also a detriment to best reception. If possible, place your antenna so that its length is at right angles to nearby utility wires. Keep your antenna clear of the walls of nearby buildings, or try and raise the antenna over the top of the building.

Many power lines, particularly older ones carrying high voltage, have poor hardware and leaky insulators which produce severe electrical interference. This will show up as a loud buzzing noise covering most of the shortwave spectrum. The farther the antenna is from the power line, the smaller will be the amount of noise pickup. Unfortunately, high voltage transmission lines can emit a loud radio racket that can be heard on a sensitive receiver a mile or two removed from the line! Orientation of the antenna for minimum noise pickup is a partial solution in such a case.

3—The antenna installation should be sturdy and well made. Occasionally you will read in the paper of a radio antenna falling across a high tension line and electrocuting the user of the receiver! Makeshift connections and haywire are definitely "out" when you erect an antenna! Stay away from power lines, and make sure that if your antenna should happen to come down, it will not hit a utility cable! If the antenna is attached to a tree, some allowance should be made for the sway of the tree in a wind. A rope, pulley, and weight should be used at the tree end of the antenna as shown in Figure 1. All joints in the antenna wires should be well soldered. In windy locations, or if the antenna might fall into the street if it came down, steel-core copper wire should be used with *strain insulators* at each end. These interesting insulators are designed in such a tricky fashion that the supporting wires will not part when the insulator breaks.

4—In locations having a great deal of moisture or industrial smoke in the air, enameled copper wire (as opposed to bare copper wire) should be used for antenna construction. Moisture and "smog" can quickly rust and corrode bare wires. As an additional protective measure, all soldered joints in the antenna system should be given a protective coat of aluminum paint.

5—*Special note for owners of ac-dc sets!* These receivers have no power transformer and one leg of the 115-volt power line is usually grounded to the chassis. To prevent shock, all controls, and the case of the receiver are insulated from the chassis. Make sure your antenna does not touch the chassis of the receiver. If you employ a ground connection, make sure the "ground" terminal of the set is insulated from the chassis, and that the ground connection is made through a capacitor within the set. If such a capacitor can not be found, make your ground connection to the receiver through a 0.01 mfd, 600 volt paper capacitor.

Armed with these five basic rules, let's examine some transmission lines, and some typical antennas that are easy to erect and inexpensive.

Antenna Resonance

For any antenna there is one frequency, called the *resonant frequency*, at which the capacitive and inductive reactances are exactly equal and neutralize each other, leaving only the radiation resistance of the antenna to oppose the flow of current in the circuit. The resonant frequency of a simple antenna is a function of its physical length. If the antenna is not the correct length for resonance at the desired frequency of operation, it can accordingly be brought into resonance by adding series inductance to equalize the capacitive reactance of an antenna that is too short, or by adding series capacitance to neutralize the inductive reactance of an antenna that is too long.

Energy Transfer to the Antenna

A resonant antenna wire suspended well in the air makes a fine antenna, but it does little good unless some means are provided to conduct the radio energy from the antenna to the receiver, or from the transmitter to the antenna. To accomplish this, a radio "hose" called a *transmission line*, or *feeder*, is used to pipe the energy back and forth between the radio equipment and the antenna. Four common types of transmission line are shown in Figure 2. Although there are physical differences between these lines, they all have the common property called the *characteristic impedance* of the line. This impedance is expressed in ohms, and is determined by the physical and electrical properties of the line, such as the size of the wire, the spacing between the conductors, and the type and amount of insulating material used. Two common impedance values of line are 52 ohms and 300 ohms. Many types of inexpensive television transmission line are available

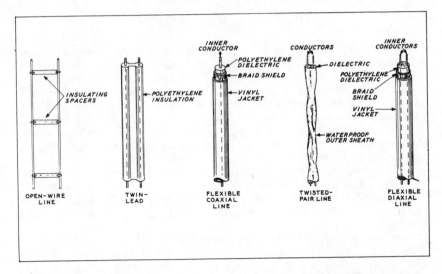

Fig. 2 Various types of balanced and unbalanced transmission lines suitable for shortwave use. The most popular types are the TV-style, 300 ohm twin lead (ribbon line) and the 52 ohm coaxial transmission line. The twisted pair and diaxial lines are rarely used except in special military equipment. The transmission line is a "radio hose", piping energy from the radio wave by the antenna down to the receiver.

in these values, and it would be a smart move to design the antenna so that it can efficiently employ these popular line impedance values.

An impedance notation of "52 ohms" or "300 ohms" does not mean that the transmission line has a resistance equal to that value. In fact, efficient lines made of copper wire have resistance values less than one ohm or so. The characteristic impedance notation of "so-many-ohms" means that the line is designed to be used with an antenna that presents that value of *terminating resistance* or *radiation resistance* to the transmission line. To clarify these last two terms, let's look at the antenna once again.

Radiation Resistance

The radiation resistance of a dipole—or any other antenna for that matter—is expressed in ohms and may be defined as that value of resistance which, when substituted for the antenna, will dissipate in the form of heat the same amount of power as is radiated into space by the antenna. The actual value of radiation resistance is determined by the length and size of the antenna compared to the radio wave, and the proximity and character of objects located near the antenna. The radiation resistance of any antenna may be measured with appropriate instruments, and usually runs in the neighborhood of 30 to 300 ohms for simple resonant antennas usually employed by both amateurs and SWLs. The radiation resistance is measured at that portion of the antenna having the greatest value of current. In the case of the dipole, this is the center of the antenna.

The Single Wire Antenna

For general shortwave reception the single wire antenna shown in Figure 1 is a hard one to beat. The *flat top* portion should be twenty to one hundred feet long for best results on all bands. The *lead-in* portion of the antenna should be as short as possible. Good, four inch glass insulators are used at each end of the flat top, and a piece of insulated wire should be employed to pass the antenna through the window or wall of the building. A lightning arrestor should be connected to the lead-in if you live in an area where thunderstorms are likely to occur. The antenna must be free of all objects and should be in the clear. Tree branches scraping against the antenna wire are likely to produce weird noises in the receiver. A simple single wire antenna of this type is relatively nondirectional, although best results will be had broadside to the wire rather than along its length. Thus, for general reception in an east-west direction, the wire should run in a north-south direction.

Most shortwave receivers have two antenna terminals and a single ground terminal. The lead-in wire should be attached to one of the antenna terminals, and the other antenna terminal should be connected to the ground terminal of the set with a short length of wire. Try reversing the connections to the antenna terminals to see which arrangement will provide best reception. In some instances reception will be improved and noise will be decreased by running a wire from the ground terminal of the receiver to a nearby ground connection. A four foot pipe may be driven into the ground for such a termination, or the ground wire may be attached to a cold water pipe in the house. A gas pipe should not be used for a ground connection.

The T-Antenna And Its Cousin, The Windom

In some instances it might be more handy to have the lead-in wire near the center of the antenna, rather than at one end (Figure 3). An antenna

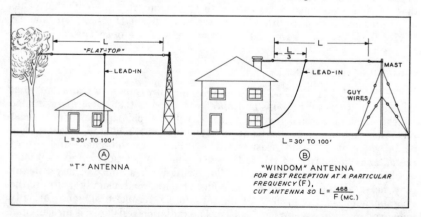

Fig. 3   A single wire lead-in may be used with your shortwave antenna. Vertical section of lead-in is particularly susceptible to pickup of man-made noise.

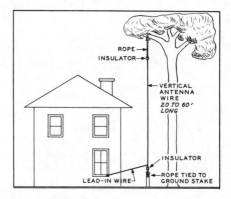

ROPE
INSULATOR

VERTICAL
ANTENNA
WIRE
20 TO 60'
LONG

INSULATOR

ROPE TIED TO
GROUND STAKE

LEAD-IN WIRE

Fig. 4 Simple vertical antenna may be supported at top end by nearby tree. Installation should be protected with lightning arrestor mounted at window sill of the house. Antenna should be kept well clear of any building.

of this type is called a *T-antenna*. The horizontal portion of the antenna should be thirty to ninety feet long, and the vertical portion can be any length. The lead-in wire drops vertically from the center of the flat top. An unbalanced version of the T-antenna is the *Windom*, shown in Figure 3B. The Windom lead-in is tapped on the flat top approximately one-third the distance from one end to provide a good impedance match between the flat top and the lead-in wire. Either type of antenna will work well at any frequency, but the Windom antenna is actually tuned to a specific frequency which is a function of length L.

The Windom antenna proves to be one of the best types intended for general shortwave reception. It may be cut for peak reception in one of the shortwave broadcast bands, or one of the amateur bands, with the assurance of good reception on all frequencies.

THE VERTICAL ANTENNA

The *vertical antenna* is shown in Figure 4. It is relatively non-directional. (As some wit once said, "The vertical antenna receives equally poorly in all directions.") This is a harsh judgment, as the vertical antenna is an excellent performer. Its main disadvantage is that it is very responsive to atmospheric and man-made noise—much more so than a horizontal antenna.

The obvious advantage of the vertical antenna is that it takes up very little ground space. It can be bolted to a chimney, or attached to the side of a house. If you live in an area free of severe automobile ignition noise and your static level is reasonably low, you might think about using some sort of vertical antenna, such as the one shown in Figure 5. A twenty or thirty foot vertical antenna will work well over the entire shortwave spectrum. The over-all length of antenna plus lead-in should not exceed about thirty feet, or antenna operation at the higher frequencies will be impaired.

THE VERTICAL GROUND PLANE ANTENNA

The *ground plane* antenna is a close relative to the vertical antenna.

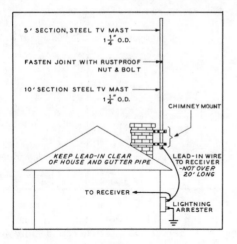

5' SECTION, STEEL TV MAST
1¼" O.D.

FASTEN JOINT WITH RUSTPROOF
NUT & BOLT

10' SECTION STEEL TV MAST
1¼" O.D.

CHIMNEY MOUNT

KEEP LEAD-IN CLEAR
OF HOUSE AND GUTTER PIPE

LEAD-IN WIRE
TO RECEIVER
-NOT OVER
20' LONG

TO RECEIVER

LIGHTNING
ARRESTER

Fig. 5 If you are surrounded by obstacles, you might consider a vertical antenna mounted to the chimney of the house. Simple TV antenna clamp may be used to hold antenna in place. Use insulated wire for lead-in, and keep it well clear of the gutter pipes.

It is simple to erect and works well over a limited frequency range, such as a single amateur band, or a shortwave broadcast band. It has a non-directional pattern, and is responsive to atmospheric and man-made noise in the same manner as is the simple vertical antenna. Dimensions of "ground planes" for various bands are shown in Figure 6. Four horizontal *radial wires* are placed beneath the antenna section. These wires act as a resonant ground screen for the vertical antenna and greatly improve reception, particularly at the higher frequencies. The radials run away from the base of the antenna, though it is not necessary that they travel in straight lines. The usual procedure is to weave them around the house, through fences, and through the garden to make them as unobtrusive as possible. The radials may slope down from the base of the antenna, but they should not project above the base level of the vertical section. The ground plane is relatively unconcerned about its location. It may be strapped to a chimney or a short pole, or placed atop a garage. As with any other antenna, it should be removed as far as possible from power, telephone, and utility wires.

This installation employs a transmission line to conduct the signal from the vertical antenna to the receiver. A length of 52-ohm coaxial line should be used. The outer shield of the line is attached to the four radials, and the center conductor is attached to the vertical section. The use of the coaxial line prevents signal pickup by any part of the antenna other than the vertical section, which is a great advantage over the simple vertical antenna of Figure 4. Noise pickup is greatly reduced, and high frequency operation is improved.

THE "FAN" VERTICAL ANTENNA

It is possible to obtain frequency coverage over the entire 3.0 to 30.0 mc spectrum with the *Fan Vertical antenna* illustrated in Figure 7. Half-dipole antennas are arranged in the form of a fan and are connected in parallel at the lower end. At resonance, each dipole section makes an approximate

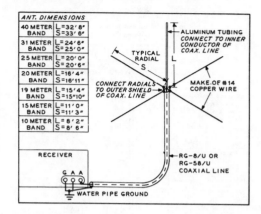

ANT. DIMENSIONS	
40 METER BAND	L = 32' 8" S = 33' 6"
31 METER BAND	L = 24' 6" S = 25' 0"
25 METER BAND	L = 20' 0" S = 20' 6"
20 METER BAND	L = 16' 4" S = 16' 11"
19 METER BAND	L = 15' 4" S = 15' 10"
15 METER BAND	L = 11' 0" S = 11' 3"
10 METER BAND	L = 8' 2" S = 8' 6"

Fig. 6 The ground plane antenna is a good performer over a small frequency band. It must be cut to the listening range for optimum results. Shown at right are antenna and radial dimensions for the most popular shortwave bands.

match to a low impedance coaxial line. The sections that are off-resonance have small effect upon the operation of the tuned section.

The fan antenna may be connected to the receiver by a length of 50 ohm coaxial line. This line may be buried underground, if desired. The outer shield of the line is grounded at the antenna end of the system by a short length of pipe driven into the ground at the point the coaxial line emerges. The shield of the line is attached to this pipe. The junction of the fan wires are attached to the inner conductor of the coaxial line. This antenna is relatively non-directional, but is more responsive to man-made noise and ignition interference than is a horizontal antenna of the same type to be described later in this chapter.

THE DIPOLE ANTENNA

The *dipole antenna* is a center fed, tuned antenna, intended for optimum receiving results over a small band of frequencies. Doublet antennas are used for reception (and transmission) by many amateurs, and are also

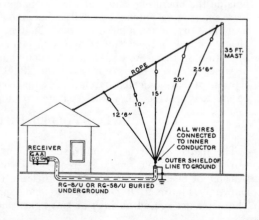

Fig. 7 "Fan Vertical" antenna is multiple system providing good reception over a wide range of frequencies. Place the antenna clear of buildings for best results.

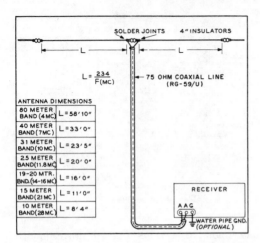

SOLDER JOINTS   4" INSULATORS

$L = \dfrac{234}{F(MC)}$

← 75 OHM COAXIAL LINE
(RG-59/U)

ANTENNA DIMENSIONS

80 METER BAND (4 MC)	L = 58' 10"
40 METER BAND (7 MC)	L = 33' 0"
31 METER BAND (10 MC)	L = 23' 5"
25 METER BAND (11.8 MC)	L = 20' 0"
19-20 MTR. BND. (14-16 MC)	L = 16' 0"
15 METER BAND (21 MC)	L = 11' 0"
10 METER BAND (28 MC)	L = 8' 4"

RECEIVER

A A G

WATER PIPE GND.
(OPTIONAL)

Fig. 8 The dipole antenna is "old standby" for good results over narrow shortwave region. Several dipoles may be erected to provide coverage of most important shortwave bands.

used for commercial shortwave circuits. The length of the flat top portion of the doublet determines the region of the shortwave spectrum to which it is tuned. The doublet is split in two at the center by a small insulator whose size is not critical. Each wire of the flat top is attached to one conductor of a coaxial transmision line. Either 52 or 75 ohm line of the type used by amateurs, or the type intended for CATV work, is satisfactory. Coaxial line, in any lengths, can be purchased in any large radio store. The length of the transmission line is not critical. It should be long enough so that it can drop away from the antenna at right angles, as shown in Figure 8.

The wires of the transmission line are attached to the two antenna terminals of the receiver. No ground connection need be used. If the receiver has only one antenna terminal, one wire of the transmission line should be attached to it, and the other wire fastened to the ground terminal of the receiver.

The dipole antenna tunes rather sharply, and optimum results are obtained only over the frequency range for which it was designed. Reception outside the operating range of the antenna will be degraded, as compared to a single wire antenna. Luckily, the dipole will work well at the third harmonic of the resonant frequency. That is, a dipole tuned to 7 mc, will also work well in the 21 mc region. Many amateurs use such an antenna for operation on the 7 mc and 21 mc amateur bands. A dipole tuned to 10 mc may also be used for reception of the 28-29.7 mc amateur band. For reception of harmonically unrelated frequencies, two or more dipoles may be erected, provided they are separated from each other by a few feet.

THE FOLDED DIPOLE

The *folded dipole* is an improved version of the simple dipole. It will work over a greater range of frequencies, and will effect a more efficient transfer of energy to the average shortwave receiver. The folded dipole is shown in Figure 9. It employs two end-connected wires in the flat top. The wires are spaced an inch or two apart, and one of the wires is broken

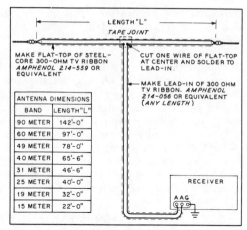

Fig. 9 Folded dipole made of 300 ohm "ribbon" line has a greater frequency coverage than the simple antenna of Fig. 8. Dimensions are given in the chart.

ANTENNA DIMENSIONS	
BAND	LENGTH "L"
90 METER	142'-0"
60 METER	97'-0"
49 METER	78'-0"
40 METER	65'-6"
31 METER	46'-6"
25 METER	40'-0"
19 METER	32'-0"
15 METER	22'-0"

at the center and attached to the transmission line.

An inexpensive version of the folded dipole may be constructed from 300 ohm TV-"ribbon line" as shown in the illustration. For greatest strength, the horizontal portion of the antenna should be made of "ribbon" having steel-core copper wire, otherwise the antenna is liable to break at the center joint in a high wind. The wires of the transmission line are attached to the receiver terminals as in the case of the ordinary doublet antenna.

THE TRIPLE DIPOLE

It is possible to combine three dipoles into one antenna to form an "all-wave" antenna system covering the range of 5 mc to 30 mc. Good reception may even be had over a wider range of frequencies if a small loss in signal strength is accepted. A typical *triple dipole* antenna is shown in Figure 10. The flat top is composed of three separate dipoles connected to each other and to the transmission line at the center of the antenna. The combined

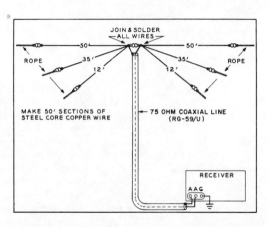

Fig. 10 Triple dipole covers broad frequency range and is recommended for general listening. Erect antenna as high in air as possible for optimum results.

frequency response of the interconnected antennas results in good reception over a range appreciably greater than that provided by two separate antennas.

The dipole wires are fanned away from each other. In most installations, the longer pair of wires are used to support the antenna, and the shorter wires are merely tied off beneath the antenna, as shown. For optimum results over the complete frequency range, a 52 or 75 ohm coaxial line should be used. The outer conductor is attached to one set of wires and the inner conductor to the other set. Be sure to waterproof the joints!

It is a good idea to make the top sections of the antenna from lengths of hard drawn copper wire, or steel core wire. This will prevent the wire from stretching under the load of the transmission line, and also will give an added safety factor that is comforting to have when the antenna coats up with ice in severe winter weather!

More Exotic Antennas

The ultimate reception is to be had with the use of beam antennas. These antennas provide optimum results in a certain direction, and must be "aimed" at the transmitting station. The usual beam antenna has a pickup lobe varying from twenty to seventy degrees wide permitting the antenna to cover a large area of the world. For example, a beam antenna user in New York could cover the whole of Europe with one high gain antenna. These specialized antennas minimize the fading and "flutter" of a long distance signal, and reduce the interference received from a signal that is "off the beam." The *Beam Antenna Handbook* and the *VHF Handbook* cover antennas designed for amateur transmission and reception on the high frequency and very high frequency bands. The reader is referred to these texts for the "real dope" concerning these interesting antennas. Both books are published by Radio Publications, Wilton, Conn., and are available at your local radio distributor.

CHAPTER IX

Reception Techniques

Shortwave reception is an art. There's more to it than rushing out and buying a receiver, hanging a piece of wire on it for an antenna, and immediately hearing exotic DX stations and having your mailbox flooded wtih verification cards! Sure, you can hear the VOA, or the BBC with a piece of damp string tied to your receiver for an antenna. But if you are looking for real DX—an amateur on the opposite side of the globe, or a weak broadcast station in Outer Slobbovia—it is necessary to absorb a few tricks of the trade. Here are some pointers that will start you on the exciting road to better DX reception.

You've got to know *how* to listen, *when* to listen, and *where* to listen! You also should have a good working knowledge of radio propagation and its effects on DX signals. Armed with these facts, you have a pretty good chance of hearing the station you are looking for. Haphazard scooting about the dial will provide a lot of fun and net some interesting stations, but the serious listener tracks his quarry like a bloodhound. Once he finds his prey he goes after the all-important QSL card with equal vigor. You, too, should "make like the bloodhound" for maximum enjoyment of this great hobby.

LISTENING HINTS

Since the ardent SWL and would-be amateur spends a good many hours at the receiver, he should try to make himself as comfortable as possible. He should make the job of receiver tuning simple, with a minimum of fatigue. The receiver can be placed in the middle of a large desk or table, slightly above elbow height when the operator is seated. The receiver is pushed back from the front edge of the table sixteen inches or so in order to allow the listener to rest his elbows on the table. The operator should sit facing the receiver, with illumination coming over one shoulder. A lamp on

Rare and exotic QSL cards from all over the world may be yours in return for sending a reception report to the many shortwave broadcasting stations. Be sure to include time of reception, wave band, selections heard, and your name and return address. Your cards will make a wonderful collection to be proud of!

top of the set gives a poor light, as it usually hits the eyes and leaves the tuning dials of the receiver in a shadow. Less light will be required if the the dials of the receiver are illuminated.

The serious DX'er uses earphones rather than a loudspeaker. Weak and semi-intelligible signals can be understood more readly when earphones are used in preference to a speaker. Room reverberation and external noises limit shortwave speaker reception to loud and steady signals. Good quality, light weight earphones of 2,000 ohms impedance will work with the majority of shortwave receivers. Low impedance (8 ohms) stereo phones are also satisfactory in most cases. Make sure the headband fits your head, and that the earpieces feel comfortable. Ill-fitting headphones can give the listener a headache after a few hours of use. Money spent in getting a comfortable headset is well worth the expense in the long run.

Operating Aids

All-important operating aids are a notebook, a pencil, and a clock. The notebook is a "must" for logging program information, dial settings, and frequency notes. The clock should be an electric one, set with radio time signals from WWV or some other accurate source. You'll need exact time so your verification data can be correct. The pencil is handy for writing in the log, and for chewing when your best DX reception is blotted out by QRM.

The log book should be used to keep a record of important facts. You should log the call letters or identification signal of the station, the time of reception (local time and GMT), program material, the signal strength, fading of the signal, and interference (if any). Other pertinent facts may be jotted down in the book at the moment you note them. The important thing to remember is that you should keep a *permanent* record of reception, as you might need it to refer back to it in the future. If you have written your notes on the back of an old racing form, they probably will end up in the wastebasket in a few days. Notebooks are cheap, and it's better to be safe than sorry! Buy an inexpensive book, and write down all your observations. You'll be glad you did, as you will create a record of your achievements that will be interesting to look over in later years.

Another important operating aid is an accurate list of all the shortwave broadcast stations, listing call letters, frequencies, and hours of operation. The *World Radio Handbook,* available through your local radio store is recommended, since it provides extensive coverage of all the important shortwave broadcast stations throughout the world.

Finally, it would be a smart move to join one of the many good shortwave listener's clubs located in the United States and in many other countries about the world. Various magazines also cover shortwave reception and give up-to-date information on shortwave stations and activities. Radio clubs come and go so no specific information about particular clubs can be given.

How, When and Where to Listen

Almost every piece of shortwave equipment you might wish to use can be purchased if you have enough money. You can read books and learn all you wish to know about antennas, receivers, and reception. You can hire a fellow to put up your antenna and align your receiver for you. *But the final results you obtain are up to you!* The technique of DX reception can be learned only by experience, coupled with patience. Spare time spent in listening and hunting for DX, and in obtaining the "feel" of the band will turn the greenest tyro into an experienced DX-chaser!

You must learn that not all weak, fluttery signals are DX. Learn to distinguish between the weak foreign signal and the watery "backwave" received from a skip-zone signal a few hundred miles away. Acquire an idea of the signal strength of some of the more powerful overseas stations so that you may use them as "light houses" to judge propagation conditions over a certain path. Just because *Radio Australia* is below par in signal strength does not mean that the less-powerful *Radio New Guinea* a few hundred kilocycles away will not be heard. The ionosphere is a mysterious device, and the strength of one signal usually bears no meaning to the strength of other signals. However, if the majority of signals from a certain direction are weaker than usual, the chances are that poor propagation conditions over this particular route will affect all signals. When the "old standbys" are putting in powerful signals it is an indication that conditions are good, and yet relatively stable. Freak reception will be at a minimum, but on the other hand you will stand a better chance of finding the weaker stations in the general period of good propagation.

You must learn what areas of the world come through at certain times of the day and night on particular frequencies. Listen to a powerful station such as the BBC that transmits the same program material on a number of frequencies. Switch your receiver back and forth between the signals. You can get a good idea of which frequency band is best for reception from the area in which the station is located. Be sure you know the source of the signal you are examining! *Radio Moscow*, for example is rebroadcast by satellite countries, and also by repeater stations in remote Siberia, and no identification of transmitter location is given. The language used in the broadcast provides no clue either, as most countries transmit many hours of foreign language programs. Careful listening, however, will log many stations that are consistent in frequency and programming enabling them to be used as marker stations for future reference. Mark them down, along with their frequencies and time of reception, so that you can look for them in the same spot another day.

Auroral "Flutter" Signals

Radio signals reaching you via great circle paths that cross the polar region suffer from auroral effects, and generally have a rapid "flutter," or "echo" on them. A listener on the East Coast of the United States, therefore, searching for stations in the Orient or the Far East should pay attention to signals that exhibit this effect. Western DX'ers, on the other hand, would observe this unusual flutter on European signals passing near the North Pole.

Signals passing through the South Pole auroral area are subject to the same type of distortion. Southern Argentina, the Falkland Islands, and the Antarctic stations can be quickly spotted by the peculiar fluttering of the carrier wave. Learn to recognize the auroral flutter signal—it means DX from across the polar region of the world!

"Long Path" Signals

There is nothing to prevent radio signals from reaching you via the long transmission path. That is, one directly opposite to the great circle route. Such propagation does occur, principally in the 6 mc to 25 mc range. Late afternoon signals from Australia and the Far East will often arrive on the Eastern Coast of the United States passing across Africa. European signals can be heard with surprising strength on the West Coast during the morning hours as they come across Australia and the Indian Ocean. These signals avoid the auroral zone, and the characteristic flutter is absent. In addition, signals from India and Central Asia may arrive via the southern path across the Antarctic continent, or across the North Pole. On many occasions, the signals may arrive by both paths. The time lag between the two different propagation paths results in a bad "echo" which usually reduces the intelligibility of such a double path signal to zero. Long path signals are often extremely strong, especially during the fall and winter months.

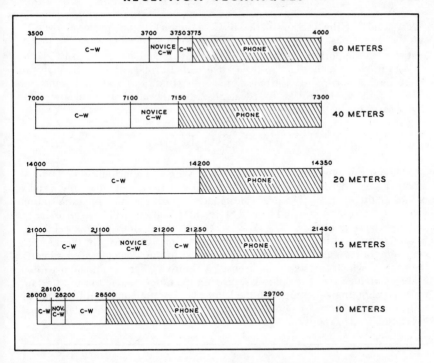

Radio hams occupy small segments of the shortwave spectrum, as shown in this chart. Listen near the edges of the American phone sections for DX stations!

Hunting DX in the Amateur Bands

Many countries that boast no broadcast facilities can be found in the amateur bands. In addition, expeditions (Operation *Deepfreeze*, for example) can usually be heard operating within the amateur bands. A tabulation of the amateur frequencies is illustrated above, with the American 'phone portions of the bands noted. Foreign SSB stations may be found both inside and outside the limits of the American 'phone band and the experienced listener will learn to listen for foreign voices in the U. S. band. Stations outside the Continental United States which are under the jurisdiction of the Federal Communications Commission (Guam, Hawaii, Puerto Rico, and other islands) operate within the limits of the American phone band.

A clue to the propagation conditions may be obtained by monitoring the local amateur phones operating in the 10, 15, and 20 meter bands. When these stations are working and calling DX, it is a sure sign that the band is "open." Since the amateur stations do not run the high power levels permitted the shortwave broadcasting stations, and since their antennas are smaller, the ham signals do not equal the strength of the b-c stations. In addition, the lower powered signals must "ride with the skip," taking full advantage of the optimum propagation conditions. For instance, the 21 mc (15 meter) band does not open for amateur work between Europe and the

West Coast of the U.S. until the BBC (London) signal peaks at over S9 on the West Coast. By the time the BBC is up to 20 decibels over S9, propagation will support the relatively weak amateur signals. If the BBC peaks to 40 db over S9, the band will be alive with European amateurs, many of them having surprisingly strong signals. As conditions wax and wane, the BBC station might still be heard at S8-9, but the amateur signals are lost by absorption in the ionosphere.

Amateur Call Letters

Amateur call letters are assigned by the FCC on an impartial basis. A typical amateur call consists of a prefix with one or two letters, a number, and a suffix of two or three letters. The prefix designates the country in which the station is licensed. In the continental United States, most stations will have an assigned call with a prefix of W, K, WA, WB, WD or N. Other short-lived, special prefixes (starting with a W, K or N) are sometimes assigned by the FCC to commemorate a particular event. The numeral in the amateur call designates the area in which the station is licensed (Figure 1). The continental United States is divided into ten call areas, bearing the numbers *one* to *zero*. Certain letter combinations starting with the letter "Q" are not employed for amateur calls, however, as these combinations are reserved for use in the international "Q-signal" code groups.

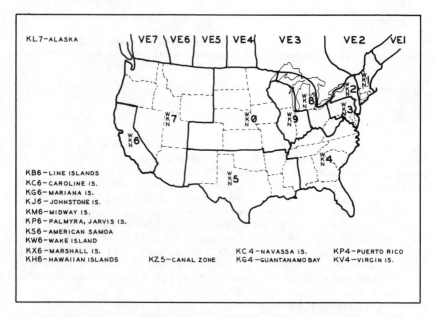

Fig. 1 United States is divided into call areas. Amateurs within these areas may be identified by the numeral in their call. The Radio Amateur Callbook lists the addresses of U.S. and overseas amateurs, and is a great help in writing for amateur QSL cards. Search the ham bands for rare DX!

Foreign call letters begin with a letter or a group of letters that usually identify the country, followed by a number and one, two, or three suffix letters. In some instances, a whole group of islands may be identified by the same prefix, so it is not always a simple matter to spot the location of the station merely from the prefix. For example, the prefix *VP2* covers both the *Leeward Island* group and the *Windward Island* group in the West Indies. An amateur station with this prefix might be located on any one of a dozen or more islands. Another famous example is the prefix *VP8*, covering the Falkland Islands, the South Orkney Islands, the South Shetland Islands, South Georgia Island, and the British Antarctic Zone. The moral of this is not to jump to conclusions when you hear an amateur call. Look the prefix up on a country list. You *may* be fooled.

Amateur Operation

An interesting group of stations for the DX-hound to hunt are the *maritime mobile* stations, operating in the 10 and 15 meter amateur phone bands. These sea-going hams are usually members of the crew of a freighter or oil tanker, and they visit the remote corners of the world. Federal law requires

The popular programs of the British Broadcasting Corporation may be heard throughout the world in all of the shortwave broadcast bands. Shown above is one of the powerful transmitters located in the British Isles that has made the beautiful tones of "Big Ben" well-known to all shortwave listeners. All major countries are represented by powerful shortwave stations such as this one.

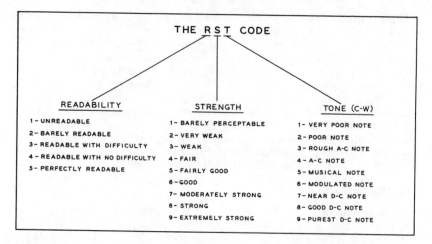

Fig. 2 The RST code is used by amateurs to permit rapid and concise transmission of signal reports. Use this form of report when QSL'ing to hams.

that the exact location of the ship be given, and you might be lucky enough one day to hear Captain Kurt Carlsen of the *Flying Enterprise II* announce, *"This is W2ZXM, maritime mobile, at 118 degrees west longitude, 35 degrees north latitude, in the China Sea."* A peek at your atlas will pin-point the location of the vessel.

Some amateur stations are engaged in handling messages between Armed Forces personnel overseas and their relatives at home. Daily contacts are maintained by many hams with the Antarctic bases scattered across the south polar continent and with other bases in Europe and Africa. Other amateurs are DX-chasers like yourself, and specialize in tracking down and contacting rare and unusual stations. You can locate GI hams in dozens of countries by monitoring these message handling stations.

Amateurs have their own language, which is a distant relative of the Morse telegraphic code abbreviations. These old abbreviations are often used "as-is" for phone work, along with modern ones thrown in for good measure. A little listening experience will enable you to "translate" this jargon into good English.

The SWL should remember one important fact when he tries to obtain a QSL card from an amateur station he has heard. The amateurs do not *ask* for SWL reports. Most shortwave broadcast station solicit reports and are morally obligated to reply to them. The ham seldom does this, and therefore the SWL takes a justifiable risk when he sends his card to an amateur station. Many hams do not reply to SWL cards, since they cannot afford the postage bill. Be sure to include an International Reply Coupon with each SWL report to an amateur if you expect to receive a reply.

The C-W Amateur

Unfortunately, most shortwave listeners are eager to log phone amateurs, but few seem to pay much attention to DX hams that operate c-w. The authors have been active amateurs for over twenty years and have received literally thousands of SWL cards and letters reporting reception of their SSB signals, but only a handful of letters confirming the c-w transmissions. None of the c-w reports came from the United States! It seems like the American SWL's shun the code more than their overseas brothers! In other parts of the world the reverse is true, since a few European countries require the SWL to obtain a license to *listen*. If he is further interested in obtaining an amateur license to transmit, he must present a certain number of QSL cards received from c-w amateurs whose signals he has heard. Consequently the c-w ham receives SWL cards from foreign listeners, but *almost never* from SWL's in the U.S.A. This is a pity, since the chances of obtaining a reply from a c-w report are many times greater than from a phone report, because a SWL card is much more of a novelty to a c-w station. Many phone amateurs are swamped with SWL cards, and ignore them entirely. On the other hand, low powered foreign c-w hams are anxious to obtain reports on their signals, and a SWL card means much to them.

If you are interested in someday obtaining your ham "ticket" you must master the code. Why not "kill two birds with one stone" by copying c-w ham stations? You can find real DX, pick up interesting and rare QSL cards and improve your code copying ability all at the same time! Over 75 percent of the amateurs outside of the United States operate c-w, so you will find unusual DX and rare countries in the c-w portions of the amateur bands.

YOUR SWL REPORT

Hearing the station is only half the battle. The other half is obtaining a confirmation of your reception. Some stations are prompt in replying, and a few never reply at all. One or two require that you send them postage. Some reply to a few reports and ignore others. By and large, the majority of broadcasters try wholeheartedly to verify all the *accurate* reports of reception that they receive. Here are a few "tricks of the trade" that will help you increase the percentage of your replies.

What should your report consist of? You might writer a letter to the station, or you can send a shortwave listener card *(SWL card)*. The card may be a home-made one, or it may be printed by a QSL card printer. Examples of some printed cards are shown in the illustration. Whatever form of report you employ, it must include some rather pertinent information if you expect the report to be of any use to the station. First of all, you must give your *name* and *address*. Don't laugh! A lot of fellows forget this all-important bit of information. Put your *full* mailing address on the card or letter as well as on the envelope just in case the envelope is put aside. Secondly, you should state the *date* and *time* of reception. Be sure to specify *what kind of time* you are using (Eastern Standard Time, Daylight Savings Time, GMT, etc.). Name the *operating frequency* of the station, or at least the approximate waveband of reception. If your report is sent to a broadcast station list the *names of the musical selections* (if you know them), or at least the *type of music* being played. Note any *announcements* you hear, and any other program information that you can obtain. Next, you should give a *reception report*, indicating the *signal strength* of the station. This report should be given in the RST code, shown in Figure 2. A phone signal may perhaps have a report of R4 S7, indicating a moderately strong signal, readable with practically no difficulty. Receivers having signal strength meters calibrated in S-units can give a close approximation of the received signal in relation to other signals on the band. The "tone" section of the RST code is used for c-w signals. It is the custom to group the report for such signals, as RST 558, for example. This indicates a perfectly readable signal of fair strength, having a pure note.

Finally, you should indicate the *type of receiver* you are using (number of tubes, etc.) and the *type of antenna* (length, height). A complete report will also indicate the weather condition and the general state of radio reception at the time the report is made.

There is an old saying: "You can catch more flies with honey than you can with vinegar"—remember this. In return for your information, you are asking the station to spend its money to have verification cards printed and mailed. The printing and postage bills for a popular station can run into many hundreds of dollars a year. A bunch of worthless reports will make the station owner think twice before he shells out his money for verification cards! Make your report as painstaking and as neat as you can. In order to relieve the financial cost to the station, please inclose several International Reply Coupons with your report. The coupons are available at most post offices for a few cents, and may be converted into sufficient postage for one piece of first class mail in most foreign countries. The IRC coupon will boost your percentage of replies, so use it!

The length of time required for a reply to a report varies widely, depending upon the policy of the station, and the speed of the mail. The average time to process a report and mail a verification card is about three months. Many stations reply in less time, but a few mail out listener reports only once a year! After an interval of six months or so, it might be a good idea to mail a second report to the station if you have received no reply, since your original report or the reply to it may have become lost en route. On the average, a return of about 70% may be expected with no particular strain or pain on your part.

Amateur QSL Cards

Obtaining QSL cards from foreign amateur stations presents other interesting problems. The report to the ham should be as all-inclusive as your report to the s-w broadcasting station. You may obtain the address (QTH) of most of the foreign hams from the latest edition of the *Radio Amateur's Callbook*, available at most radio supply houses. This will enable you to send your report of reception directly to the amateur. Be sure to incude an IRC coupon with your report. Certain countries—particularly the "Iron Curtain" ones—are a little "touchy" about their amateurs receiving direct mail from overseas. The hams in these countries have therefore set up QSL clearing houses which operate from a postal box, usually located in the capital city of the country. All incoming and outgoing QSL cards must pass through this semi-official clearing station. A SWL card or letter sent to "Amateur Radio Station so-and-so" in the Soviet Union would either end up in the clearing station, or in the wastebasket of the censor.

Unfortunately, the hams behind the "Iron Curtain" cannot or will not reply directly to QSL and SWL cards. All replies pass through their QSL

"So it's only 9 p.m. in the Fiji Islands!
Get out of your dugout canoe and come to bed!"

bureau to the QSL bureaus of other countries. The amateur QSL bureaus of W-land do not handle SWL cards, and unless special arrangements can be made through one of the larger SWL clubs, your chances of receiving a verification card from a ham in one of these countries is pretty slim.

Save Your Cards and Reports!

As you become an experienced listener, your stack of verification cards will grow. Be sure to save them! A large photographic album is a fine place to exhibit the cards, and offer them protection at the same time. Two prized cards in the author's collection of over 4000 QSL's are the first SWL verilcation cards he received in 1930.

RADIO TIME

Since Columbus proved he could reach the east by sailing west mankind has run into a number of problems arising from the fact that the earth is round. One of these problems intimately concerning the SWL and the amateur is the fact that the local time is not the same at different points around the earth. When it is midnight in Los Angeles, it is 3 a.m. in New York, 8 a.m. in London, 11 a.m. in Erevan, noon in Teheran, 4 p.m. in Manila, 7 p.m. in Noumea, and 10 p.m. in Honolulu. In addition, it might be Sunday morning in New York, while it is Saturday evening in Manila!

As you can imagine, computing the time in a particular part of the world could turn out to be a bit tricky, especially since some countries as Ceylon,

GMT TIME CHART											
CALCUTTA	SINGA-PORE	MANILA	TOKYO	SYDNEY	WAKE IS.	FIJI IS.	HAWAII	FAIR-BANKS	SITKA	PACIFIC STANDARD TIME	MOUNTAIN STANDARD TIME
0600 +6 H	0700 +7 H	0800 +8 H	0900 +9 H	1000 +10 H	1100 +11 H	1200 +12 H	1300 −11 H	1400 −10 H	1500 −9 H	1600 −8 H	1700 −7 H
MONDAY				MONDAY NIGHT		← DATE LINE →		SUNDAY MORNING			SUNDAY

Fig. 3   Greenwich Mean Time (GMT) is universal radio time. It is based on time in Greenwich, England and is used with a 24-hour clock. No notations of "am" and "pm" need be used. Time is correlated with longitude degrees.

India, British Guiana, and Indonesia have their own particular time. Saudi-Arabia takes the first prize in the confusion contest, as it has no local standard time. A twelve hour time period starts at sunrise and sunset, and the starting time of each period changes since the sun rises at a different time each morning! "One o'clock" in Arabia means one hour after local sunrise, and differs from day to day.

Some years ago the British helped to solve this knotty problem by adapting a 24 hour clock, and establishing time zones throughout the world based upon this clock. In addition, the new time system had nothing to do with the local time, as it was based upon the time of a standard clock located in Greenwich, England. This system is called *Greenwich Mean Time* (GMT) and is not so nutty as it sounds. After all, our conception of time is purely arbitrary. We could get along just as well if our days were divided into thirteen hours instead of twenty-four. We could make each day fifty hours long by making each hour shorter. The concept of "a.m." and "p.m." is also artificial, since the clock hands point only to numbers. We mentally add the idea of "afternoon" or "morning" to the time we read on the clock. Greenwich Mean Time does away with all this balderdash in one drastic revision. Since Greenwich is located on the zero degree meridian, GMT is tied directly to degrees of longitude. Thus, if you know where you are, you know your time compared to the time in Greenwich, England. The position of the sun in the sky has nothing to do with your local Greenwich time. If your location happens to be *east* of Greenwich, your local time will be *ahead* of GMT, and if you are *west* of Greenwich your time is behind GMT. In either case, you can express your time in Greenwich hours.

The 24-Hour Clock

GMT is based upon a 24 hour clock, instead of the usual 12 hour clock we are familiar with. Thus, in the GMT system 9 a.m. is 0900 hours, 1 p.m. is 1300 hours, 5:30 p.m. is 1730 hours, and 11:55 p.m. is 2355 hours. The notations of "a.m.", "p.m.", and "minutes" are not required. Since GMT is based upon the idea of longitude, any point in the world may reckon its time relative to GMT *if* the degree of longitude is known. New York, for instance is west of Greenwich and its local time is 5 hours behind GMT. 8 a.m. in New York is therefore 1300 GMT. Singapore is east of Greenwich, and its local time is 7 hours ahead of GMT. 4 p.m. in Singapore is thus 0900 GMT. This simple (?) situation is summarized in Figure 3. The important thing to remember is that if you express your local time of

GMT TIME CHART											
CENTRAL STANDARD TIME	EASTERN STANDARD TIME	ATLANTIC STANDARD TIME	RIO DE JANIERO	AZORES IS.	DAKAR	(GMT) LONDON	CENTRAL EUROPEAN TIME	(MSK) MOSCOW	ADEN	SVERD- LOVSK	BOMBAY
1800 −6H	1900 −5H	2000 −4H	2100 −3H	2200 −2H	2300 −1H	2400 0	0100 +1H	0200 +2H	0300 +3H	0400 +4H	0500 +5H
SUNDAY					SUNDAY NIGHT		MONDAY MORNING				MONDAY

If you know where you are, you know your time compared to GMT. If you are east of Greenwich, your local time will be ahead of GMT, and if you live west of Greenwich, your time is behind GMT, as shown in the above table.

reception in GMT, the station to whom you send a report will be immediately able to translate the time of reception into its own local time. It can then cross-check your report easily. In fact, many shortwave stations and amateurs use GMT as their "station time" instead of their own local time.

Figure 3 shows a conversion chart for all the time zones of the world. Look up your time zone and convert your time into GMT. You can also tell GMT time in other areas of the world from this chart. Learn to use it. It will be a big help in aiding you to translate world time systems.

Time Signals

Many stations throughout the world transmit time signals on various frequencies. The stations you will probably use the most are the *National Bureau of Standards Stations WWV and WWVH* located in Colorado and in Hawaii respectively, and the *Canadian Dominion Observatory Station CHU* in Ottawa. *WWV* and *WWVH* announce the time each minute in Universal Time (UT=GMT), and *CHU* announces each minute in EST. Listeners in the Pacific areas can use *JJY*, Tokyo or *WWVH*. A table of time signal broadcasts is given in Figure 4.

In addition, *WWV* announces a radio propagation forecast for the North Atlantic path at 18 minutes past each hour; the forecasts are updated every six hours. Also, there is a verbal description of propagation conditions for the present and immediate future. Check *WWV* for a quick summary of radio propagation conditions and compare the information with the radio conditions at your location.

THE SHORTWAVE BROADCAST BANDS

Jumping from broadcast reception to shortwave reception requires quite a reorientation on the part of the listener. No longer are the stations spaced at modest 10 kilocycle intervals across the band. Instead, the shortwave stations are packed into the spectrum in what seems to be a haphazard fashion. The listener will find broadcast stations intermingled with code transmissions and with each other in an apparent state of chaos. However, there is some method in the apparent madness, and most shortwave broadcast stations are grouped into broadcasting "bands," or segments of the spectrum. These areas are relatively free of code and radio teletype interference, and here you will find the majority of DX broadcast stations. The bands are the 90 meter band (3200-3400 kc), the 60 meter band (4750-5060 kc), the 49 meter band (5950-6200 kc), the 41 meter band (7100-7300 kc), the 31 meter band (9500-9775 kc), the 25 meter band (11700-11975 kc), the 16 meter band (17700-17900 kc), the 13 meter band (21450-21750 kc), and the 11 meter band (25600-26100 kc).

A quantity of broadcast stations operate outside the limits of these bands, however you will find that the majority of shortwave broadcasters stick pretty close to these internationally recognized regions.

Each shortwave broadcast band has its own peculiarities of propagation, depending upon the time of day, the season of the year, and the sunspot cycle. Let's look at these bands and see what general conclusions we can reach about them.

The 90 and 60 Meter Bands

The 90 and 60 meter bands are primarily used for local coverage broadcast work in the tropical areas. During the evening hours of the winter months it is possible to hear many South and Central American stations in these channels. The high static level reduces the utility of the 90 meter band during the summer months, but the 60 meter band is useful the year around. Many medium and low power Spanish speaking stations come and go in this frequency region, and some of the signals are quite strong.

The 90 meter band is almost exclusively populated by South and Central American stations, but the "DX-bloodhound" will find many 60 meter African signals from the Congo, Angola, Kenya and the Republic of South Africa wedged between the Latin signals. In the early hours of the morning you might hear some of the Far East broadcast stations, such as Port Moresby, Papua New Guinea. Russian and Chinese regional services can also be heard in the hours before dawn stateside.

The 49, 40, and 31 Meter Bands

These three bands form the "backbone" of shortwave broadcasting, as they contain a majority of the s-w stations of the world. Over a hundred countries compete for your ears amid this beehive of electronic activity. These bands are all-year performers, and are "open". most of the hours of the day and night, with conditions peaking just before sunrise, and during the evening hours. The static level is much weaker than on the lower frequencies, and the main interference comes from the multitude of signals. As many as eight or ten stations operate on the same channel during the hours of the day or night. If propagation is right, you may hear several stations from different parts of the world at the same time on the same spot on the dial. The din that is created is amazing!

The "lighthouses" on these bands are the *Voice of America*, the BBC *Radio Moscow*, the *Canadian Broadcasting Commission*, *Radio Australia*, the *Voice of Brazil*, and others too numerous to mention. Buried beneath the "big" signals are a wealth of weaker stations. The experienced DX-er finds this his "happy hunting ground," and he combs the bands avidly for signals from *Radio Monte Carlo*, Karachi, Pakistan, Brazzaville, the Gilbert Islands, Ceylon, Tahiti, Austria, Greece, Syria, and a host of other exotic places. Often, the radio conditions conspire to project a station above its comrades on the dial. A fluctuation of the ionosphere and *Radio Sweden*

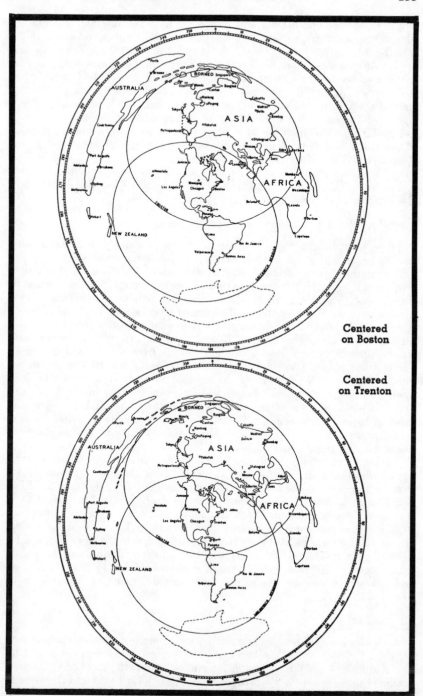

**Centered
on Boston**

**Centered
on Trenton**

will fade out and the listener will be treated to a few fascinating moments of entertainment from New Guinea, Cameroons, Cyprus, or some other far-off spot. Indonesian, Chinese, Malaysian and other Far-Eastern signals are heard consistently on the West Coast of the United States, and many of the more powerful ones are received in the Eastern part of the United States

Reception during the evening hours in the 41 meter band is chaotic, since it overlaps the 40 meter amateur phone band. The loud, local amateur signals obliterate all but the most powerful broadcast stations.

Popular inhabitants of the 31 meter band are the "down under" stations of Australia and New Zealand. Listen for the powerful signal of *Radio Australia* and the laugh of the Kookaburra bird, native to Australia. The song "Waltzing Matilda" signals the popular transmissions of this station. *Radio New Zealand* of Wellington features the call of the Bell Bird, while *Radio Sarawak* strums an identifying guitar.

The 25, 19, 16, 13, and 11 Meter Bands

These four bands, high in frequency, are considered seasonal bands. During periods of great sunspot activity, the ionosphere will support propagation at these frequencies. A steady migration of stations to the higher frequencies takes place over a period of years. Except for the bottom of the sunspot cycle, these h-f bands will support reliable communication for most of the year. However, during the summer months, the 11, 13 and 16 meter bands will be erratic, exhibiting their best characteristics during the fall and spring season. The 19 and 25 meter bands are all-year performers. As the sunspot cycle wanes, a gradual exodus from the 11 and 13 meter bands takes place. The movement soon spreads to the 16 and 19 meter bands, and when the bottom of the sunspot cycle arrives, as it will once again, the higher frequency bands will be deserted most of the year. The erratic conditions and "dead" periods will reduce the reliability of transmission to the point where it is no longer economically practical. A few hardy perennials, like VOA and the BBC may "hang on" during the lean years, but the signals will be few and far between.

Although the total population of the four highest frequency bands never approaches that of the 49, 40, and 31 meter bands, their propagation conditions at the crest of the sunspot cycle are excellent. Signals from the BBC and *Radio Australia* may be heard over the United States for hours at a time, with strength rivalling local broadcast stations. A star performer at 21.455 kc are the *Voice of America* transmitters in Tangiers, Morocco and Dixon, California. The backwave from the broadcasts to the Near East can be heard across the United States. "Down" on 16 meters, Radio Nederland with transmitters in Holland and Malagasy, provides refreshing musical request and talk shows, happily free of the "commercials" that clog American programs of this type.

"Jammers"

A continuing pest on all bands is the multitude of jamming stations run by Russia, China and other Communist countries. Their purpose is to blot out broadcasts from the U.S. (and sometimes from each other!). A group of jammers often render a SW band useless. A backward salute to the success

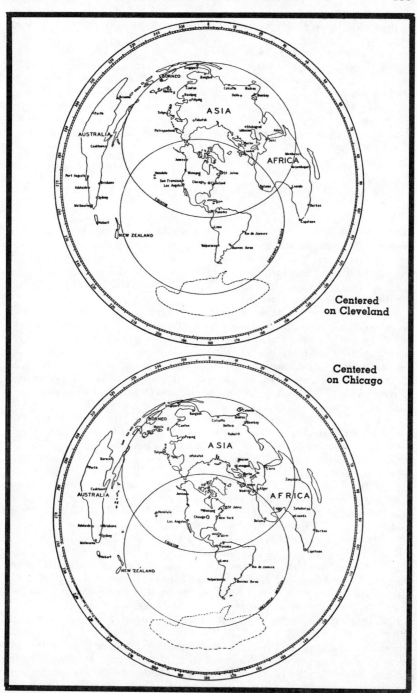

Centered
on Cleveland

Centered
on Chicago

of these programs is the swarm of jammers that lie athwart the broadcast bands, trying to strangle free speech. At one moment the air is clear, with no interference. The VOA will start a native language broadcast to some Soviet Republic, and the band will erupt with buzz-saw signals. As many as 25 jammers at one time have been counted in the 21 mc band. Each jammer has an identifying coded signal of one or two characters. With an atlas and a little imagination you can soon pin-point a number of the furry things on the map. Pity the poor SWL or ham living near one of these creatures! It is interesting to speculate on the effectiveness of this kind of interference. Usually, it is merely annoying, as the trained listener can often "hear through" the jamming signal.

A Bandspread Scale for Your Receiver

Many modern shortwave receivers have bandspread tuning dials. The bandspread dial provides vernier tuning action, permitting more accurate tuning and logging of stations. This dial takes a small segment of the short-wave spectrum and "magnifies" it over the entire rotation of the bandspread scale. Most dials of this sort are calibrated "0-100", and a few are calibrated in kilocycles for the amateur bands. Practically none of them are calibrated for the shortwave broadcast bands.

With a sheet of graph paper, a pencil, and a few hours' listening time, you can make calibration curves for each shortwave broadcast band, as inter-preted against the markings of the bandspread dial. This curve will assist you in hunting down stations known to be active in the region covered by the calibration. With care, frequency readings accurate to two or three kilocycles may be made. You should make curves for the 11, 13, 16, 19 and 25 meter bands. Calibration curves for the low frequency bands often will come in handy, too. Here's how:

First of all you need an accurate frequency list of the major shortwave broadcast stations. An excellent list is provided in the *World Radio Handbook*. Let's assume you wish to make a calibration chart covering the 13 meter band. Accurate frequencies must be logged in kilocycles rather than meters, so we'll refer to this band as the 21,450-21,750 kc band, and we will calibrate our graph in terms of kilocycles. Make up a chart as shown in Figure 5, with the frequency range placed on the horizontal axis, and the bandspread dial range marks on the vertical axis. We'll also assume that your bandspread dial reads "100" with the bandspread capacitor open, and "0" with the capacitor fully meshed. Start with the dial reading of "0', and adjust the main tuning dial until a station on the low frequency edge (21,450 kc) of the band is heard. The *Voice of America* relay station in Tangier, North Africa is a fine band-edge marker. It operates on 21,455 kc (21.455 mc), right on the "low edge" of the band. Another fine marker for you is the *VOA* station in Greenville, S.C. at 21,485 kc. Readjust your dial so that Tangier falls about "5" on the bandspread dial. If you are working with Greenville, place it about "12½" on the bandspread dial. This setting will give you a little extra "room" at the edge of the band. Note the setting of the main dial, and mark it down in a corner of the graph. The next step is to mark a point on the chart where the dial reading of the marker station and the frequency of the station meet. For the Tangier station, the coor-

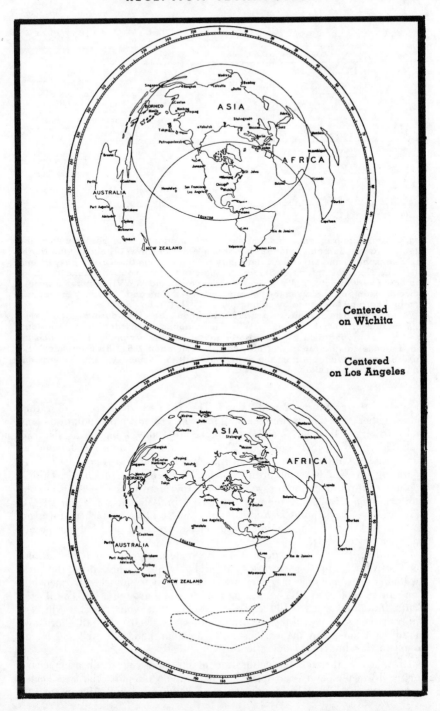

Centered
on Wichita

Centered
on Los Angeles

CALL	LOCATION	FREQ. (MC.)	TIME TICK	MODULATION ∿	POWER (KW)
LOL	BUENOS AIRES, ARGEN.	5.0,10.0,15.0	YES	440 1000	2.0
ZUO	JOHANNESBURG, REPUBLIC OF SO. AFRICA	2.5,5.0	YES	—	4.0
RWM	MOSCOW, USSR	10, 15	YES	—	—
MSF	RUGBY, ENGLAND	2.5, 5.0, 10	YES	1000	0.5
JJY	TOKYO, JAPAN	2.5,5,8,10,15	YES	1000	1.0
IBF	TORINO, ITALY	5.0	YES	440 1000	5.0
—	UCCLE, BELGIUM	2.5	—	—	0.02
CHU	OTTAWA, CANADA	3.330, 7.335, 14.67	—	1000	3.0
WWV	FT. COLLINS, COLO.	2.5, 5, 10, 15	YES	440 1000	10
WWVH	KAUHI, HAWAII	2.5,5,10,15			

Fig. 4　Standard frequency and time signals are broadcast from many points on the globe. National Bureau of Standards stations WWV and WWVH blanket the Northern Hemisphere, and the other signals may be heard in the U.S. CHU is easy to find, also. The National Bureau of Standards stations feature voice announcements of the time every minute. WWV utilizes a male voice, and WWVH features a female voice to distinguish between the two stations. WWV time and frequency broadcasts can be heard by telephone by calling (303) 499-7111 in Boulder, Colorado.

Voice broadcasts of radio propagation conditions are given during part of every 18th minute of each hour from WWV. The announcements deal with short-term forecasts of propagation over the North Atlantic paths. Complete information on the Services can be found in NBS Special Publication 236, NBS Frequency and Time Services, available from the Superintendent of Documents, U.S. Government Printing Office, Washington, DC 20402.

dinates of the graph are 2 and 21,455. This is one end of your calibration curve. Other well known marker stations will provide more points. Let us look further up the dial. Wait! Here is the BBC at 9½ on the bandspread dial. This must be their outlet on 21,480 kc. Mark an appropriate spot on your graph. A little farther we run into WNYW *(Radio New York)*. It is operating on 21,590 kc, according to the *World Radio Handbook*. This is another calibration point for your graph. Now here is the *VOA* in Dixon, California on 21,630 kc, followed by KGEI in Belmont, Calif. on 21,370 kc. The next check point is *Radio Peking* on 21,745 kc. Mark it down on the graph! Now, if you examine your chart, you will see that the points fall on a smooth line.

Of course, the examples given here are imaginary ones, and the stations you'll use for calibration purposes will probably not be these ones. But pick the louder ones, and ones that stick pretty close to their published frequencies. You can be fooled, as SW stations do tend to jump around a bit. *The World Radio Handbook*, plus a 100 kc crystal oscillator in your receiver will certainly assist you in making accurate calibration charts for all shortwave broadcast bands, and the various radio amateur bands as well. So let us complete this imaginary operation.

Draw a line through the calibration points, and your calibration curve for the 13 meter band is completed. Now you can pin-point the frequencies of any stations in this band right on your bandspread dial. If you wish to

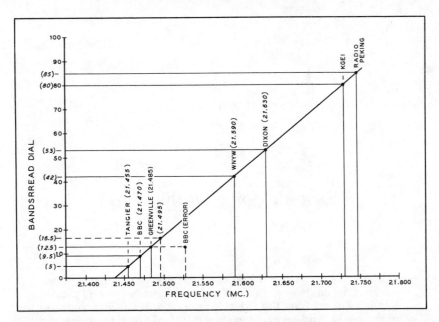

Fig. 5 It is easy to make a calibration chart for the bandspread dial of your receiver. Plot the frequencies of stations against the dial reading on a sheet of graph paper as shown above. The frequency of other stations may then be found from the graph. This example is for the 15 meter band.

find *Radio Nacional* in Portugal on 21,495 kc, you will tune to "16½", and that's where they will be, *provided* you always re-set the main tuning dial so that the known "marker" stations fall at the proper bandspread dial calibration points.

This system is very handy, but it is not absolutely foolproof, as some of the s-w broadcast stations have a disconcerting habit of hopping and skipping about on the dial as they try to find an interference-free channel. Some of the smaller stations, too, are not always on frequency, drifting about slowly during their programs. However, once you set your dials correctly and know the approximate frequency of your quarry, you can hunt it down like a bloodhound! Make up a set of charts, one for each shortwave broadcast band, and you will find that they will help your DX-efforts a thousand percent!

You can make up a set of bandspread calibration charts for each amateur band, if you wish. It is a little harder to obtain calibration points in the ham bands, as the amateurs do not usually announce their operating frequency, and they hop about the band with more gusto than do the s-w broadcasting stations. Even so, the high frequency and low frequency edges of the phone band may be approximated at the point where the din drops off, and the Canadian and foreign amateurs appear. The same approximation my be mde for the edges of the c-w bands where an abrupt cessation of c-w activity is noted. After several listening periods you will be able to accurately mark the band edges on your chart.

CHAPTER X

Eavesdropping on the World

**Don't rely on hearsay! You can hear the world's news direct,
yourself, by shortwave radio. You can hear news — and propaganda — direct from the capitals of most of the larger countries
of the world. And an exciting story it is, too! You'll hear, too, the
smaller countries — Israel, Canada, Ecuador, Arabia — that
speak with a loud radio voice and have special programs
beamed to America. Closer to home, the VHF bands include the
police, fire and public service frequencies. You can ride the
"prowl car" during the evenings, and follow the fire engines
in your town from your armchair. Monitor the airport control
frequencies and hear the big jets as they arrive and leave. All
these activites, and more, are as near to you as the dial of your
shortwave receiver!**

You, the experienced shortwave listener, will soon realize that a tremendous
amount of communication activity goes on in the radio spectrum both "above"
and "below" the standard broadcast band (see Figure 1, Chapter II). A good
working knowledge of "where the action is", plus patience and a naturally in-
vestigative philosophy, will reward you with a fascinating new realm of radio,
beyond the imagination of the casual listener who spins rapidly across the dial,
seeking the louder broadcasters. A lot of the "action", moreover, takes place
in the low frequency (LF), very high frequency (VHF) and ultra high frequency (UHF) bands, for which special receiving equipment and unusual
antennas are required for good reception.

By international agreement, the radio spectrum is divided into various
bands, of which the most popular and well-known to listeners are the shortwave
international broadcast bands and the radio amateur bands. Other bands exist
which provide interesting reception for the informed "eavesdropper". For
example, good listening may be had in the marine and aeronautical bands, the

YAESU FR-101 "all-wave" receiver covers twenty-one 500 kc ranges from 160 to 10 meters, including amateur bands and the major shortwave broadcast bands. Frequency readout is accurate to 100 cycles.

FM broadcast band, the bands reserved for police, fire and municipal service, aeronautical and mobile communications, and space communications bands. In addition, the long wave broadcast band is of more than passing interest. You, the listener, equipped with knowledge and the proper receiver can discover endless hours of enjoyment and instruction monitoring the radio spectrum in depth — not simply scanning the international broadcasting stations. Here's a quick summary of what is in store for you!

A TOUR OF THE RADIO SPECTRUM

Long Waves (10 kc to 550 kc). This portion of the radio spectrum was the birthplace of long distance radio communication around the time of World War I. It still has important uses today and provides interesting reception for the sophisticated listener who has learned to copy the International Morse code. Some inexpensive three-band transistor radios cover the "radio beacon" portion of this range immediately below the broadcast band but for serious listeners a special converter or a war-surplus long wave receiver, a long antenna, plus a quiet, noise-free location are necessary for proper reception. Unfortunately, the sweep oscillators of nearby television receivers create ragged interference to long wave reception and good listening in metropolitan areas is very difficult.

Communication stations which send c-w and teletype messages inhabit the lowest portion of the long wave range (10 kc to 70 kc). You'll hear Navy stations such as NLK, 18.6 kc (Washington); NAA, 17.8 kc (Maine) and GBR, 16.0 kc (England) among others. These super-power stations broadcast enciphered traffic, plus messages and news in English at 20 to 25 words

CONTINENTAL ELECTRONICS giant megawatt broadcast transmitter speaks to the world with a powerful voice. A number of these million watt output transmitters are in service overseas. Maximum broadcast power in USA is limited to 50,000 watts.

per minute. They're usually on 24 hours a day and these "radio lighthouses" are easily heard throughout the United States, even with a simple receiver. These low frequencies are more reliable than shortwaves, are less affected by ionospheric disturbances, and can be received by submerged submarines at great distances from home.

Above 70 kc (in the United States) are many radio positioning beacons and weather stations. Some avid listeners have converted surplus radio tele-type printers and facsimile machines (which print weather maps from radio impulses) so that copy and log these stations. Of greater interest, however, is the 150 kc to 260 kc portion of the band which is widely used for broadcasting in Europe and Asia. On a quiet winter night on the east coast of the U.S., European broadcast stations can be heard with good signals, often as far inland as Colorado. On the west coast, the long wave outlets of *Radio Moscow* in Siberia, *Radio Peking* and *Radio Mongolia* may be heard. A DX band for the night owl, the long wave broadcast band is at its best during winter nights and provides an interesting and little-known hunting ground for the advanced listener.

Above 450 kc or so, ocean-going passenger ships and freighters chatter with each other and with shore radio stations, using c-w. The international distress frequency (500 kc) is just below the broadcast band; this frequency is also

the commercial "calling" frequency for ships. When distances of over a few hundred miles must be covered, ships use the high frequencies (6 - 18 mcs). If you copy messages to and from ships, remember the rules of privacy and do not discuss or disclose what you copy.

THE BROADCAST BAND (540 KC TO 1600 KC)

This "entertainment" band is used world-wide for domestic broadcasting. The American formula of 10 kc spacing between channels reduces adjacent-channel interference and permits the listener to tune for European signals, which have different channel spacing. Many of the high power overseas stations, therefore, fall into the frequency gaps between the local U.S. stations. During winter nights on the east coast, some of the more powerful European and South American broadcasters may be heard on a sensitive, selective receiver. On the west coast, Australian or New Zealand stations may be logged, along with an occasional Japanese, Russian or Chinese signal.

THE HIGH FREQUENCY BANDS (1.6 MC TO 30 MCS)

Aside from radio amateurs and super power international broadcasters, a host of other intense activities crowd this portion of the radio spectrum. Short distance ship-to-shore contacts are in the 2 mc to 3 mc region; 2182 kc is the common distress frequency. Many amateur and commercial single sideband (SSB) stations exist (see pp. 26-27) which provide the listener an insight into the day-to-day affairs of the world. Military and aircraft SSB circuits and nets (many stations on the same frequency) are plentiful in the HF spectrum, as are MARS (Military Affiliate Radio Service) stations which specialize in overseas telephone traffic between the military and their home-based families. These voluntary service stations, manned primarily by radio amateurs, are usually found just outside the limits of the HF amateur bands. Near the frequencies of the MARS nets, too, may be found slow speed military stations transmitting c-w, which is ideal for code practice.

In addition to this traffic, point-to-point and marine radiotelephone traffic takes place on SSB, sometimes with the use of "voice scramblers" to insure secrecy; a scrambled signal sounds like Donald Duck only less intelligible; However, a certain portion takes place in plain English and makes interesting listening. Extended observation will provide a pattern of operation of many of these stations. Most transmissions are extremely short and you must be "on your toes" to hear them; once you catch on to the jargon the going is smoother — and most interesting.

Luxury liners and yachts on distant cruises use SSB "high seas" circuits between 8 mc and 16 mc and you will come across them from time to time talking to unfortunates left behind in the office or home. These circuits are usually not scrambled.

Listening to radio amateurs handling messages ("phone patches") to stations in the Antarctic, to distant ships and to foreign countries is an absorbing

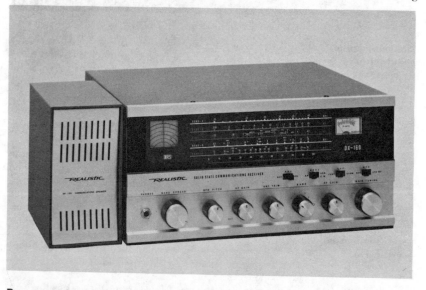

Representative of the medium-priced shortwave receivers is the Realistic DX-160. This imported receiver covers 535 kHz to 30 MHz, and also the long wave spectrum between 150 and 400 kHz in a fifth band. The DX-160 features electrical bandspread and may be operated from the power line or from an external 12 volt d-c power supply. It is available from Radio Shack Corp.

PIONEER radio amateur experimenter Paul Wilson (W4HHK, Collierville, Tenn.) uses backyard "dish" antenna to bounce two-way radio signals off the moon. Using microwaves, W4HHK's transmissions aimed at the moon have been reflected back to earth and received by other amateurs who detected the waves after they had travelled nearly a half-million miles through space. Other radio amateurs in Europe and Australia have talked with each other and with the USA by means of moon-reflected radio signals. Highly directional antennas, extra-sensitive receivers and high power transmitters are required for this feat. Some amateurs have automatic tracking systems coupled to their antennas so that the radio beam follows the moon as it progresses across the sky.

SWL pursuit; most ham patching is at the high frequency end of the 20 and 15 meter bands. (Remember not to discuss what you hear.)

On occasion, "pirate" broadcasters may be heard, operating from a ship off the European continent, or perhaps an island near a scene of conflict. As international control of radio broadcasting becomes more effective over the years, the pirate station tends to become a thing of the past. Modern pirates seem to be clandestine stations set up in areas of world tension, usually with the covert backing and support of one of the quarreling powers. Pirate broadcasts are sometimes the first source of important international news and have played key roles in some of the uprisings in the eastern European countries. An alert ear should be kept during periods of high international tension and you'll often hear the news as it happens!

Digital Transmission

On the high frequencies you will hear stations sending peculiar bursts of what sounds like random noise, or a buzz saw. These staccato signals are known as "digital transmission" and are the most modern method of safe (secure) communication used by the military services. In essence, the secret message is transformed into "computer language" which can be understood and re-

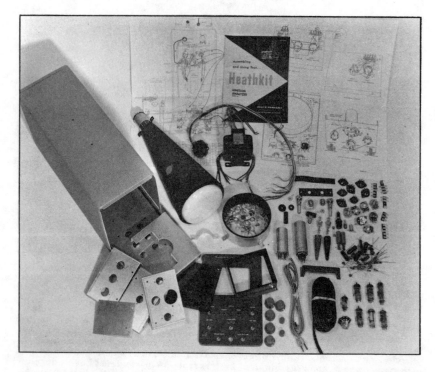

RADIO EQUIPMENT, including receivers, stereo gear and oscilloscopes (above) come in kit form for fast assembly. Complete instructions make task easy for builder.

turned to English only by another computer on the receiving end, which is privately clued in. What is transmitted is not fast c-w, but bursts of digital computer language. One computer, in effect, is "talking" to another which, hopefully, will make sense out of what appears to be nonsense.

The equipment used for digital transmission is extremely complicated, in fact so complex that vital messages sent by this means are sometimes misrouted, delayed or never received. It is believed that the messages sent to the intelligence ship *USS Liberty* telling it to withdraw from the coast of Israel, and the difficulty the *USS Pueblo* experienced off the coast of North Korea in sending an urgent message to Japan about her predicament are examples of failures of this transmission mode. If the electronic transmitting and receiving equipments are not in synchronization, they cannot understand each other and the message is lost, or received too late to do any good, as was in the case of the *USS Pueblo*. A sound argument may be made that the military may sometimes be too entranced with systems so exotic and impenetrable that the message never gets through. In radio communications, as elsewhere, common sense is often a scarce commodity.

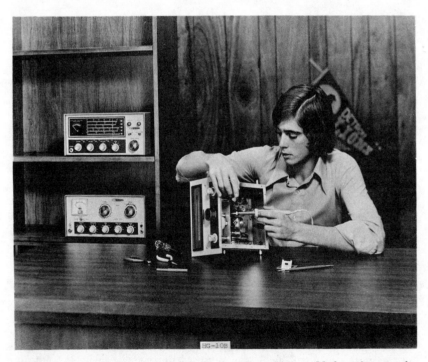

BEGINNER ASSEMBLES HEATHKIT shortwave equipment. Modern, inexpensive kits are available for the newcomer which provide first-class equipment at a modest cost. Usually a screwdriver, pliers and soldering gun are the only tools required to assemble a kit. Advanced experimenters may assemble a stereo, an electronic organ or a color television set from packaged kits.

INEXPENSIVE portable receivers such as this "Patrolman 9" (Radio Shack) tune the three public service bands, the aircraft band, and FM, as well as the AM band and HF from 1.6 to 22 mc. This unit has a BFO so single sideband can be received.

RADIO SCIENCE AND THE LISTENER

It is possible for an alert listener to make a real contribution to the science of radio communication. The following is a case in point:

During the early "sixties" some avid listeners in the southwestern U.S. reported and logged broadcasts from *Radio Stanley* in the Falkland Islands off the tip of South America. The signals were heard in broad daylight near 80 meters when this portion of the spectrum is "dead" for long distance signals. No other listeners reported these signals. The question arose—why were these curious long distance signals heard by these listeners and no others, and why in only a very small area around California and Arizona?

The listeners finally enlisted the aid of the Radioscience Laboratory of a large California University. A study of the ionosphere and continuous 24 hour monitoring of the mysterious signal revealed long distance radio propagation by a hitherto unknown mode. similar to the propagation along the magnetic field of the earth used by "whistlers"—lightning generated, low frequency noise. *Radio Stanley's* signals were propagated into outer space. to the furthest reaches of the earth's magnetic field. and returned to a small spot in the northern hemisphere by a highly curved path. A truly amazing new propagation mode had been discovered by some persistent SWL's who recognized an unusual signal when they heard it! It's not possible for every listener to become a Columbus of the airwaves. but all listeners should carefully investigate unusual signals that do not conform to the common reception pattern.

EARLY BIRD communication satellite hovers over equator at altitude of 22,300 miles, relaying 240 two-way voice telephone circuits between Europe and North America. Newer, larger satellites can handle 1,000 two-way voice circuits.

LISTEN TO THE WORLD'S NEWS AS IT HAPPENS

Don't rely on hearsay! You can hear the world's news direct, yourself, by shortwave radio. You'll hear the news — and propaganda — on the hour and half-hour — direct from the capitals of the larger countries of the world. And an exciting story it is, too. Since the main "radio language" is English, you can take an "arm chair" tour of the world at leisure. The louder stations that broadcast directly to North America will be noticed first. London, Berlin, Moscow, Rio, Prague, Tokyo — all will be logged, along with hundreds of others to choose from. *Radio Peking*, speaking from Red China makes particularly interesting listening, bombarding the western ear with vituperation and bombast that is amazing to hear.

Besides this dazzling international display of nationalism among the big powers, the smaller countries often speak with a loud radio voice. Ecuador, Canada, New Zealand, Israel and others have special programs in English, as do many of the eastern European Countries and Russian Republics. If you are interested, many countries provide their audience with language lessons, which can be valuable and interesting. Your shortwave receiver becomes your private tutor at no cost, with lessons in French, Spanish, Russian, Japanese or Swahili!

THIS 85-foot antenna located at Hawaii earth station is used to transmit and receive communications to and from Pacific satellites. Station links Hawaii with US mainland, and USA with Asia.

Citizens Band (CB) Radio

A unique radio service exists at 27 mc on your shortwave dial. Created in 1958 to provide personal radio service for the citizen, this narrow range now has over 2,000,000 licensed private radio stations in the United States, with additional thousands licensed overseas in foreign countries. Crammed into closely spaced channels, CB stations are intended for personal business for the individual and private enterprise, utilizing simple, low power two-way radiophone equipment. Over the years, the availability of low priced, imported radio gear and the pleasure of socializing by radio has altered the CB picture and a large percentage of today's CB activity is purely social in nature. The widely-used, cheap, imported walkie-talkie which requires no radio license to operate has turned the CB channels into a nightmare in many cities, and thoughtless interference has reduced CB to chaos in much of the United States. Despite the "chatter" problem and interference, a great volume of worthwhile communication is carried out by CB operators and their low power stations in automobiles and at home. Many a serious highway accident is first reported by a CB operator and help speeded on its way and CB assistance is often provided to police and civic organizations through intelligent use of CB radio — all of which makes good listening.

Amateur Radio

Blended in among the many shortwave stations you'll hear c-w transmissions. Many amateur stations transmit code, as well as various point-to-point stations and military stations. It's not very difficult to learn the code, and a

CITIZENS TWO-WAY RADIO provides low cost communication for business and pleasure — at home, in the car or on vacation. Any U.S. citizen over 18 years old may apply for Citizens Band (CB) radio license. No test and no special skills are required. CB radio works much like a party-line telephone. Press the microphone button and call your party — release the button and listen. CB radio license is obtained by writing your local Federal Communications Commission Field Office and asking for application Form 505 for Class B-C-D Citizens Radio Station License. F.C.C. offices are located in Mobile, Anchorage, Los Angeles, San Diego, San Francisco, San Pedro, Denver, Washington (D.C.), Miami, Tampa, Atlanta, Savannah, Honolulu, Chicago, New Orleans, Baltimore, Boston, Detroit, St. Paul, Kansas City (Mo.), Buffalo, New York, Portland, Philadelphia, San Juan, Beaumont, Dallas, Houston, Norfolk and Seattle. The telephone book listings are under "U.S. Government".

SWISS radio amateur John Raetz is pioneer VHF experimenter, using "dish" antenna to bounce signals to the moon and back to Puerto Rico and to the USA. Station HB9RF also contacted many radio stations using the OSCAR amateur radio satellite which repeated "ham" signals back to earth as it circled the globe. John and his group of Swiss and German amateurs are leaders in VHF experimentation.

whole new world of listening will open once you have mastered the alphabet and numerals. Then, too, knowledge of the code is the first step towards a radio amateur license which permits you to transmit on the amateur shortwave bands.

The amateur license is issued by the Federal Communications Commission upon the applicant's proof of knowledge of regulations governing amateur radio, knowledge of basic amateur practice, knowledge of the code and sufficient technical knowledge to correctly operate and maintain transmitting and receiving equipment. The first step is to start learning the code. Some think that copying code is a stumbling block, but actually all that is really needed is willpower and concentration, as over 200,000 amateurs have proved. To get started on your way, write to the American Radio Relay League, 225 Main St., Newington, Conn., 06111 for copies of these inexpensive booklets: 1)—*How to Become a Radio Amateur*. 2)—*Learning the Radiotelegraph Code*. 3)—*The Radio Amateur's License Manual*. Memorize and practice the code and study the simple rules and theory in the ARRL books. Sooner than you thought possible, you'll have your amateur radio operator's license and a whole new world of enjoyment and learning, new friends, and exciting public service will open before you. Who knows, amateur radio might even change the course of your life — it has for thousands of people!

THE VERY HIGH FREQUENCY (VHF) BAND

Above 30 mc radio waves, generally speaking, are confined to line of sight distances, except when special communication equipment is used, or unusual propagation conditions exist in the atmosphere. VHF waves may occasionally be reflected from ionized bits of the atmosphere, bouncing a signal back to earth at a distant point. VHF ionospheric reflection, however, decreases rapidly with increasing frequency and is quite rare above 100 mcs or so.

The lower portion of the VHF spectrum is a region of great interest because of the unusual propagation conditions that exist from time to time. Most of the communication in this range takes place on frequency modulated systems, which provide great rejection of man-made noise. Accordingly, an FM receiver or standard receiver with an FM adapter must be used for good reception. In this radio region are the police, fire and public service bands. You'll hear real-life drama in the making, before it hits the newspaper headlines, or the local radio or TV flash. You can follow the prowl cars and monitor airport control frequencies, and hear the big jets talking as they arrive and depart, and keep track of them, too, as they wing their way across the continent!

The first "service" band covers 30 mc to 50 mc. Inexpensive, imported FM receivers may be bought, or built from a kit, which tune this region. An efficient antenna is particularly important on VHF and suitable "ground plane" whip antennas may be purchased to do the job.

From 55 mc to 88 mc TV channels 2 through 6 exist, followed by the 88 mc to 108 mc FM broadcast band. Some listeners monitor the TV channels and the FM band for long distance reception, and TV stations in South America and Europe are occasionally logged in the United States.

The frequency range from 108 mc to 154 mc is reserved for aeronautical services, airport approach control stations, radio amateurs and mobile services. Again, special receiving antennas cut to a specific length are almost essential for good reception.

Transmissions between commercial and private aircraft and airport control towers, to and from control centers along flight paths, make the most interesting listening in this portion of the spectrum. Brief in duration, and using special jargon, it takes time for the listener to understand what is going on.

THE RADIO AMATEUR TWO METER BAND

From time to time, radio amateur space stations (OSCAR satellites) transmit in the 2 meter (141 to 148 mc) amateur band using a short coded message, or retransmitting amateurs in relay fashion. Lucky is the listener who logs one of these "birds". At times, too, long distance amateur contacts spanning oceans and continents are made by signals in this band which are literally bounced off the moon as a "radio mirror" and picked up, half-way around the world. Large antennas, powerful and sophisticated equipment plus skill and experience are essential for this feat. By far the greatest use of the 2 meter amateur band is for local "rag chewing" in the larger metropolitan areas of the country. It makes interesting listening for the city-SWL.

Above Two Meters

Above 148 mc and up to about 175 mc is a second large band which contains additional FM services (fire, police, taxicabs, forestry and industrial communication). Suitable FM receivers for this band, too, may be bought in the larger radio supply stores. It must be remembered, however, in some areas of the country a permit must be obtained from the local police or sheriff's office to place a VHF receiver in an auto or truck that is capable of receiving police broadcasts. It's wise to check with your municipal authorities before installation of such gear in your auto to avoid running afoul of the law. No permit, of course, is needed for home reception.

The Ultra High (UHF) Frequencies

As the listener leaves the public service band, he enters the fascinating UHF world. It's in this range that today's exciting developments are taking place, for this is the region of satellite relay systems, astronaut communication and radio astronomy.

UHF receiving systems are complex and costly, and are usually designed to accomplish a specific task. Even so, advanced amateurs have received photo transmissions from weather satellites and have listened to the astronauts as they prepared to set foot on the moon. A listener in Angola, Africa, has monitored most of the transmitting satellites put up by the United States and Russia with homemade equipment. School boys in England, monitoring Russian launches with surplus receiving gear, have discovered a hitherto secret Russian space launching site by careful study of intercepted satellite signals.

Listening to a satellite is an unrewarding experience unless you possess special decoding equipment; all you hear are bursts of sing-song tones, running up and down a limited scale. These telemetry signals yield valuable scientific data when processed, but are gibberish to the SWL.

Radio Astronomy

First noticed by a radio amateur in 1938, radio "noise" has been found to emit from the Milky Way and from the planets. Today, over 350 radio telescopes have pinpointed thousands of discrete radio emanations, many of which have yet to be identified with optically visible objects in the universe.

Each year, more hobbyists join the ranks of radio astronomers; most enthusiasts belonging to amateur astronomy groups. Some radio noise sources, such as the sun and the planet Jupiter, can be picked up with a standard shortwave receiver and a simple antenna. The hissing radio noise from the sun can be heard during all radio "blackouts" on the higher frequencies and is quite apparent at all times above 30 mc when a directional antenna is pointed at the sun. The radio noise from Jupiter may be heard at night when the shortwave bands are dead, sounding as the surf breaking on the beach over a wide band of frequencies from 6 mc to 20 mc. At times, the Jupiter "hiss" is quite strong, easily heard on a portable receiver with a whip antenna.

For more information on radio astronomy, the book *Radio Exploration of the Planetary System*, by Smith and Carr (D. Van Nostrand Co., N.Y.) is recommended.

Astronaut Communication

Early U.S. orbital space flights used a HF SSB radio link between the astronaut and earth. The voice of the astronaut circling the globe could be clearly heard near 15 mc on a good communications receiver. It is reported that Russian cosmonauts still employ HF voice communication to the earth and such transmissions may be found near the 10 mc and 15 mc frequencies of WWV. Modern U.S. space telecommunications, however, now take place in the UHF region in the range of 1550 mc to 5200 mc, and in the VHF range between 240 mc and 300 mc.

During the launch, ascent, earth orbit and splashdown phases of space flight, communication from vehicle to earth is maintained in the VHF range, and these signals may be heard by the experimenter using a sensitive VHF receiver and a small beam antenna. Apollo-8, for example, used 259.7 mc and 298.8 mc for voice communication.

When the vehicle is in outer space, communication and data transmission *(telemetry)* takes place in the UHF band and voice, television, tracking and ranging information are transmitted on a unified system over one radio link. Good reception of such signals requires highly specialized receivers and large antennas, such as shown on page 150.

A world-wide tracking network exists during a space flight and includes both land-based stations and ocean-going tracking ships. These are linked by undersea cable and HF SSB circuits. The network often rebroadcasts the UHF transmissions of the space craft. A search of the 10 mc to 18 mc spectrum during space operations may disclose this network and makes fascinating listening of history in the making.

Looking Ahead

What will the next decade bring in the way of new modes of long distance communication? Radio satellites are now used for intercontinental relay of voice, TV and data information; television relay from the moon of live pictures was accomplished in 1968. Looking to the future, space satellite broadcasting of radio and TV direct to home receivers may become a reality. It is reasonable to assume that the microwave frequencies (above 1000 mcs) will be used to transmit from the ground to the satellite. The satellite, in turn, might retransmit the program to receivers on earth (over a full half-hemisphere) in the FM band, or possibly the UHF TV band.

Programs will be televised live and in color from places with names hard to pronounce and even more difficult to spell. Radio and TV communication to the home will go world wide, opening a whole new horizon of reception to the listener as he searches the microwave spectrum for satellite rebroadcasts.

Even so, the HF spectrum will not become obsolete, and will remain a happy hunting ground for the DX enthusiast, using the improved receivers, antennas and equipment of the next decade.

So good hunting and Better Shortwave and Microwave Reception for 2001!

About the Authors

WILLIAM I. ORR — started out as an SWL (shortwave listener) in 1929 and obtained his first radio amateur license in 1934 (W2HCE). In 1937, he became one of the first 'phone stations in the world to earn the coveted WAC (Worked All Continents) award. He received his E.E. degree from Columbia University and the University of California and spent five years during and after World War II designing and building electronic equipment for Douglas Aircraft Co. Licensed as W6SAI in 1938, he rose to world-wide prominence as a DX operator by 1950, through the use of efficient beam antennas which he designed and built. The author of over 100 electronic articles for various magazines, the "Beam Antenna Handbook", "All About Cubical Quad Antennas", and other popular books, he is the editor of the authoritative "Radio Handbook". An executive with a large California electronics company, he still finds time to be active on the ham bands and to write articles and books.

STUART D. COWAN — built his first shortwave receiver in 1931 and passed the amateur license examination in 1932 (W2DQT). In 1935, he was a radio operator and technician with the Grenfell mission in Newfoundland and Labrador. Following his graduation from Princeton, he spent five years in the Navy in World War II and saw action in the Atlantic, European and Pacific theaters as a communications and electronics officer. On D-Day in the Normandy invasion, he improvised an emergency destroyer fire control circuit which provided a key radio link, for which he was decorated. He has designed and built electronic equipment, and received a citation from the National Academy of Sciences for 'phone patching South Pole personnel to their families during the 1957 International Geophysical Year using his amateur station. A former vice president of Raytheon, a large electronics company, he has written articles and books, and is an active ham radio and CB operator (W2LX, W1RST, KCZ1102).

BETTER SHORTWAVE RECEPTION

INDEX

OTHER BOOKS FOR RADIO AMATEURS, CB OPERATORS, SHORTWAVE LISTENERS, STUDENTS, EXPERIMENTERS

SIMPLE, LOW-COST WIRE ANTENNAS FOR RADIO AMATEURS, by William I. Orr, W6SAI; 192 pages. $4.95

All-new! How to build tested wire antennas, 2 thru 160 meters -- horizontal, vertical, multiband trap and inexpensive beams. Special! "Invisible" antennas for hams in "tough" locations. Antenna tuners; baluns; new data. "A truly practical Handbook, gives no-nonsense dope, "--Carl Lindemann, Jr., W1MLM, Vice President, NBC.

ALL ABOUT CUBICAL QUAD ANTENNAS, 2nd edition by William I. Orr, W6SAI; 112 pages. $4.75

The revised edition of this famous Handbook contains: new Quad designs; new dimension charts; new gain figures; analysis of Quad vs. Yagi. Building data, tuning information; new, studier construction. Much data never before published! "A storehouse of new information",--KH6IJ; "Packed with useful data", W6AM.

BEAM ANTENNA HANDBOOK, 4th edition, by William I. Orr, W6SAI; 200 pages. $4.95

The 4th edition of W6SAI's popular Handbook contains correct dimensions for beam antennas, 6 thru 40 meters; data on triband and compact beams; SWR curves; how to save money by building your beam. A "must" for the serious DXer whether he buys or builds his antenna. "This Handbook is my bible",--Gus Browning, W4BPD, editor, "The DX Bulletin". "Vital for DXers who want results",--5Z4ERR.

VHF HANDBOOK FOR RADIO AMATEURS, 1st edition, by Herbert Brier, W9EGQ and William Orr, W6SAI; 336 pages. $5.95.

All new! This new edition of the popular "VHF Handbook" covers VHF from A to Z, FM theory, operation, equipment, repeaters. All about VHF antennas, including new Log Periodic and Long Yagi designs. Exciting information about satellite and moonbounce communication. Long distance VHF DX propagation and how to use it. "Important VHF information for all radio amateurs",--Barry Goldwater, K7UGA, U.S. Senator from Arizona.

THE TRUTH ABOUT CB ANTENNAS, by William I. Orr, KCK 3201/ W6SAI and Stuart D. Cowan, KCZ1102/W2LX; 240 pages, $5.95
This clear, fun-to-read Handbook gives the CB operator all he needs to know to buy (or build) install and adjust, efficient CB antennas for powerful signal. The unique "truth table" unmasks false antenna claims--shows exact gain results from 10 most popular antenna types. Covers all types of CB antennas from A to Z. "A great CB antenna Handbook!", George Wood, KBI3274/ W1SR, Transistor Marketing, RCA.

CARE AND FEEDING OF POWER GRID TUBES, by Robert Sutherland, W6PO, and the Laboratory Staff of EIMAC. 158 pages. $4.95
This Handbook analyzes the operation of power grid tubes and provides design and application data for long tube life and maximum circuit stability. An ideal book for the serious communicator. Used as a text by leading engineering schools.

HOW TO BUY THESE BOOKS:

Leading electronics distributors and dealers, and selected book stores, sell these popular handbooks. Buy them at the store nearest you.... On orders to publisher, please add 35¢ per book for postage and handling. Connecticut residents please add sales tax.

RADIO PUBLICATIONS, INC.
BOX 149, WILTON, CONN. 06897